PAIN-LESS

PAIN-LESS

ANNE WELSH

SilverWood

Published in 2019 by SilverWood Books

SilverWood Books Ltd
14 Small Street, Bristol, BS1 1DE, United Kingdom
www.silverwoodbooks.co.uk

ISBN 978-1-78132-904-7 (hardback)
ISBN 978-1-78132-875-0 (ebook)

British Library Cataloguing in Publication Data
A CIP catalogue record for this book is available from the British Library

Page design and typesetting by SilverWood Books
Printed on responsibly sourced paper

For all the people I love and for those who love me.
You have made my pain painless.

An honest and insightful account in to a world unknown to so many. Having spent her life living with this inherited blood disorder, Anne's Christian faith, courage, determination and hope in the midst of adversity shines through as she charts each stage of her life living with sickle cell disease. With helpful pointers throughout both for those living with sickle cell and for friends and family supporting, this is a resource worth reading. As Anne comments, 'never let your illness define who you are and make you afraid' – Amen to that is what I say!

The Most Revd and Rt Hon. Dr John Sentamu
Archbishop of York

I have the utmost respect for those who suffer from sickle cell disease. The pain I have seen them experience is just awful and the suffering is immense. Any help for people to learn how to avoid pain triggers and handle their pain better is to be welcomed, as in this book based on the life and experience of Anne Welsh.

Professor Dame Sally C Davies DBS FRS FMedSci
Chief Medical Officer For England

Most people suffering from diseases or ailments are always reluctant to discuss their experiences in public let alone committing such experiences into a book form for all to read. Anne has got over the shyness and the inhibition and has put her experiences and how, with the support of family, loved ones, friends and her doctors and with the grace of God, she was able to 'live painlessly with pain and make the best out of life'. It is a must read for victims of sickle cell disease, family members of sufferers, handlers and colleagues of victims of sickle cell or sufferers from any chronic illness or disease.

Olusegun Obasanjo
President of Nigeria from 1999 to 2007

The best books are those that harness personal experience to help others. That's what this book is: a powerful account of Anne Welsh's own journey with her "invisible illness"; a valuable resource for sufferers of sickle cell anaemia; and an important reminder to those of us in public health of our duty both to ensure people like Anne can access the care they need, and to work towards a cure.

Dr Tedros Adhanom Ghebreyesus
Director-General of the World Health Organization

CONTENTS

PREFACE

I was born with sickle cell anaemia, and while it is not a unique medical condition, it has influenced the way I live my life in so very many ways. Some might say that it has restricted me or held me back and, once, maybe I would have agreed – particularly when I was growing up. But now? Now, I realise that every cloud has a silver lining. And every experience can make you stronger. I can't pretend that it's been easy, and there have been moments of extreme physical pain, which have sent me into the depths of despair. But I have come to a place in my life where I have come to terms with my illness and have found a way to control it, rather than allowing it to control me. Sickle Cell Disease (SCD) can be devastating to live with – both for the sufferer and their family – but I hope that by telling my story and sharing some of the lessons I have learned along the way, I can help other sufferers and their families. Because, despite the chronic pain and the frequent illness, it is possible to lead a full and happy life provided you manage the disease well, and take good care of your mental and physical health.

While I was growing up, I often thought that my life would never amount to much, that I would be reliant on my family forever. But gradually over the years, I have come to terms with SCD and have found a way to live life well and happily. It hasn't been easy, and there have been many, many setbacks along the way – as you will see when you read the book – but I have reached a point where I feel peace and contentment, and I wish the same for all my fellow sufferers and for anyone suffering from an invisible illness.

You will notice that I refer to sickle cell as an invisible illness frequently throughout the book. This is because to the outside world, sufferers look healthy and well, and even happy. But the truth is so very different for many of us. Inside, our body has turned against us, and we suffer continual pain – sometimes manageable, but sometimes so excruciating it takes our breath away. Yet still, we look well, so people often don't understand that we may need help or support, whether physical or mental – because the mental consequences of living with chronic pain can be severe.

What follows is the story of my journey and of the lessons I have learned to help me overcome the stresses and pain of living with sickle cell. I know that there will be much here that my fellow sufferers can relate to and I hope that what I have learned will be useful to others too.

For me, learning to live with sickle cell has meant finding a way to come to terms with the physical pain and to accept that life can be wonderful, even though it is full of uncertainty and sometimes I am limited as to what I can do. It has been a mental battle that I have fought throughout my life. And now, finally, I feel I have made friends with my disease. Without doubt it is a troublesome and inconvenient friend at times, which demands attention when I'd rather ignore it, but I have accepted now that – good and bad – this friend is here to stay.

I hope for all my fellow sufferers that perhaps my story

can help you. And that some of my advice might resonate with you and give you hope.

And for all the families of sufferers, I hope I can bring some ideas to help you support your loved ones. I know that watching someone you love suffer is awful but, believe me, without you there, our suffering would be a million times worse.

INTRODUCTION

Sickle cell anaemia rarely graces the covers of magazines or newspapers. It is almost never included in UN initiatives nor does it have many Western-backed sponsors, despite being the most common genetic disease in the world. Estimates of how many babies are born with sickle cell disease each year varies between 300,000 and 500,000, but what isn't in doubt is that up to fifty per cent of these children will die before the age of five. SCD mostly affects black populations of African and Caribbean origin, but it also affects Arabic, Indian, Southern and Central American communities, as well as Middle Eastern and Caucasian populations from Southern Europe.[1]

Migration has meant that thousands of people are living with the disease in North America and Northern Europe. In the United Kingdom, it is estimated that there are currently about 15,000 sufferers, and approximately 350 babies are born with it each year. As such, it is a significant and under-recognised global health issue.

Interestingly, the reason the incidence of sickle cell gene has become common in Africa is because the sickle

1   http://www.unesco.org

cell trait gives some resistance to malaria during childhood. But, wouldn't you just know it, if you have full-blown sickle cell anaemia, then, as well as all your other problems, you will not be immune. In fact, malaria is a major cause of death in children with sickle cell anaemia.[2]

The World Health Organization suggests that SCD may contribute to up to five per cent of deaths of children under five years old on the African continent and up to sixteen per cent in some high-prevalence countries (Nigeria, where I am from, being one of those). This puts it on a par with other, better-funded, global health problems, including HIV/AIDS (one per cent), measles (one per cent), and meningitis (three per cent).[3] Unfortunately, because of the lack of awareness and recognition of the problem by both public and local health ministries, SCD remains a largely invisible global health issue. However, steps are being taken to try to address this. For example, in an attempt to improve awareness, the UN established a World Sickle Cell Day in 2008. This falls on 19 June each year and is marked with various events worldwide.

In addition, I was delighted to read recently that in the United States President Trump is committed to supporting research to develop a cure for SCD that is available to all people, expanding on the achievements of current treatment options. Clinical trials to accelerate the development of new gene- and cell-based therapies within the next five to ten years will be conducted as part of the National Institutes of Health's Cure Sickle Cell Initiative, which launched in 2018. Additionally, there will be initiatives to better train healthcare

2   WHO Report, 2006

3   McGann, Patrick T. 'Time to Invest in Sickle Cell Anemia as a Global Health Priority', *Pediatrics,* June 2016 https://www.ncbi.nlm.nih.gov

providers to identify individuals with SCD and improve the quality and continuity of their care from infancy through adulthood.

WHAT IS SICKLE CELL?

Sickle cell disease is a genetic disorder of haemoglobin – the oxygen-carrying protein in the blood. It is not contagious, and it can only be inherited when both parents carry the sickle cell trait.

The disease owes its name to the fact that when you suffer from SCD, the red blood cells take on the shape of a sickle, as opposed to the round shape of a healthy cell, due to the haemoglobin clumping together. This means that the cells carry less oxygen and they can get 'stuck' in the smaller blood vessels, causing severe pain to the sufferer and a depletion of oxygen to their vital organs. These painful episodes are called sickle cell crises. On a day-to-day basis the problems associated with the disease – lack of oxygen in the blood, anaemia, pain – tend to be continuous, although the intensity of that pain fluctuates.

There are various types of sickle cell disease that one can suffer from, the main ones being:

Haemoglobin SS disease – the most common type of sickle cell disease, which occurs when you inherit copies of the haemoglobin S gene (the sickle cell gene) from both parents. This is also one of the most severe forms of the disease – and sadly the one I suffer from – with patients suffering frequent crises throughout their life.

Haemoglobin SC disease – this is the second most common type of sickle cell disease. It occurs when you inherit the haemoglobin C gene (which causes slight abnormalities in the haemoglobin, resulting in anaemia) from one parent and the haemoglobin S gene from the other. Individuals with SC have similar symptoms to individuals with SS. However, the anaemia is less severe.

Haemoglobin SB+ (beta) thalassemia – this affects the size of the red blood cells, which are reduced because less beta protein is made. If inherited with the HbS gene, you will have haemoglobin S beta thalassemia. Symptoms are not as severe.

Haemoglobin SB 0 (beta-zero) thalassemia – this fourth type of sickle cell disease involves the beta globin gene. It has similar symptoms to HbSS anaemia. However, sometimes the symptoms of beta-zero thalassemia are more severe. It is associated with a poorer prognosis.

There is also haemoglobin SD, haemoglobin SE and haemoglobin SO, but these types of sickle cell disease are more rare and usually don't have severe symptoms.

The type you end up inheriting is predicated on several factors that include the specific form of abnormal haemoglobin you suffer from and, obviously, the genes you inherit from your parents. Which is why couples with a history of sickle cell disease in their family should undergo genetic testing before having children, just to ensure that there is no risk of your child being born with the disease.

SICKLE CELL SYMPTOMS
Sickle cell causes chronic pain and severely inhibits any form of physical activity. The lack of oxygen in the blood also causes anaemia, which leads to exhaustion and listlessness.

The pain caused by the disease can sometimes be acute, chronic or a combination of the two. Chronic pain in SCD is not simply a continuation of the pain of vaso-occlusion (a medical term for a sickle cell crisis), it is usually secondary to avascular necrosis (the death of the bone tissue due to a lack of oxygen) of bone at various joints – e.g. the hips, knee, shoulders and ankles. But chronic pain does not just affect the body, it's also imprinted on our brain, which means that sufferers live in fear of their next crisis, and this can cause depression and anxiety.

I am often asked what sickle cell pain feels like and for me there are no words to describe it, but if I must try, all I can say is that it is like someone using a hammer to knock on your bones over and over again. This extreme pain is the result of the body being starved of oxygen, resulting in the muscles cramping and contracting. Your body needs oxygen to work – but with sickle cell, there just isn't enough, and when the oxygen levels in the blood decrease, the cramping gets worse and worse until it feels like arrows shooting through your entire body. That is sickle cell pain, and it doesn't go away.

The pain that sufferers experience differs in intensity from crisis to crisis and can last anywhere between a few hours to a few weeks. Some sufferers experience only a few episodes, while others, like me, face many more in terms of frequency and intensity.

Sickle cell sufferers are also at high risk of suffering several other serious problems caused by the lack of oxygen in their blood and the cumulative and negative effects of sickle cell episodes on the body – which means the more episodes you suffer, the more complications you can get as you get older, as organs are damaged by the frequent decreases in oxygen supply. As a result, we are at high risk of suffering from other problems such as stroke, lung problems, heart attacks, blindness, liver problems and gallstones. In addition to this, the psychological effects of the disease can be devastating.

As you can see, the consequences of sickle cell are far-reaching, severe and frequently life-threatening, so it's a disease that brings with it a reduced life expectancy. This is particularly true in the developing world where treatment is too expensive for many people to afford.

However, if managed correctly, and as new treatments become available, life expectancy has greatly improved, particularly in the West, and adults can expect to live into their sixties, provided they look after themselves well.

TREATMENT

Sickle cell is usually treated with pain medication – ranging from over-the-counter remedies to morphine during a crisis. Blood transfusions, physical therapy and psychological therapy are also important in maintaining the physical and mental health of sufferers as far as possible.

For me, medication, especially my painkillers, has been the best way of managing my illness without totally denting the quality of my life. The drugs I take vary depending on the intensity of my pain and they have been a life-saver for me on more than one occasion. At the same time, blood transfusions help prevent complications and reduce the level of anaemia by diluting the sickled red blood cells and increasing the level of oxygen in the blood. These procedures have also improved my heath by leaps and bounds.

Unfortunately, though, there is no cure for sickle cell. Currently, most treatment focuses on managing the symptoms, rather than treating the cause i.e. finding a way to prevent the blood cells from 'sickling'. And currently, the only cure for the disease is to have a bone marrow transplant. Unfortunately, this is not a viable treatment for most sufferers as not only is a bone marrow match difficult to find, the operation carries significant risks.

However, new drugs are being trialled now, and one in particular, GBT440, has been shown to have some very beneficial effects when combined with a healthy lifestyle.

PART 1

MY SICKLY LIFE AND ME

CHAPTER 1

AND SO IT BEGINS

My mum describes my birth as her 'miracle'. At the time, my parents had just moved back to Nigeria from England as my father had got a wonderful new job. We lived in a spacious bungalow with three bedrooms and a very large garden and had a German shepherd dog called Jack whom I absolutely adored.

I was born at one o'clock on a cloudless Sunday morning at the Ridgeway Hospital in Kaduna, a northern state in Nigeria.

My birth, I'm told, was easy. My mother had a swift labour without any complications, despite the fact that I arrived a few weeks before the due date. Clearly, I was impatient and raring to go, even as a baby. She tells me that I was her perfect little girl and she couldn't wait to get me home and introduce me to her perfect little boy – my brother, Eric. Her life felt complete.

Apparently, I was an easy baby; I did what all babies do – slept and ate. My mum describes it as a happy time as my father was excelling at work and she had her young family to look after. I am told that from the moment I was born, our family experienced an incredible streak of luck: my parents' lifestyle improved drastically and all their close friends attributed that growth to my birth. And so my father decided I was the family's lucky charm and that my middle name should be Chiagoziem, which means 'God has blessed me'.

However, this was all to change. In December 1980, my parents travelled to the east of Nigeria for a Christmas break. I was about six months old at the time and my mother had noticed something unusual about my body. My arms and stomach had swollen. She was confused and the only plausible explanation she could think of was that my nanny at the time may not have been feeding me properly. Times were hard in Nigeria and it wouldn't have been unusual for the nanny to have taken some of that food to feed her own family. My mother confronted her about the issue, but she insisted that she was doing everything that she was supposed to.

My mother became increasingly worried, as over the next few days the swelling remained the same. Of course, a six-month-old can't articulate what is wrong and my mother and nanny exhausted all the usual techniques to get the swelling down. But it wasn't going away, and finally my mother took me to the university hospital in Enugu to see a paediatrician. To my mother's shock, the doctor told her, rather abruptly, that I was a 'sickler' and dismissed her, giving her no hint of what this could mean for either her or me. Because of his rudeness and disinterest, my mother decided that he probably didn't know what was wrong with me and took me home not much the wiser. She continued to give me general medication, and eventually the swelling disappeared and she put the doctor's diagnosis to the back of her mind.

It was the 1980s in Nigeria and even doctors, let alone my family, knew little about sickle cell. The disease had not even been given a formal name until 1910. Furthermore, little had been done in terms of research and general awareness. In addition to this, in Nigeria there was a huge stigma attached to sickle cell anaemia. Many believed it was somehow linked to witchcraft, so not a lot of people were comfortable talking about it and sharing the diagnosis with even close family.

In fact, my mother had not been aware that she carried the sickle cell trait until she had my brother. He had been born in Hedon Road Maternity Hospital in Hull. When they gave her the news that she carried the sickle cell trait, she decided not to breastfeed as she thought the condition was contagious and at the time the staff at the hospital knew very little about the disease so were not able to advise her properly. This is typical of the lack of information available at the time to describe and treat the disease. But they gave her a blue card to show to doctors in case she ever needed an operation as she would need oxygen during the process.

After this incident with me, life went on as normal and in January 1981 she was pregnant again and decided she wanted to move back to the UK to advance her teaching studies in London. She wanted to start afresh. My father was frustrated as he was happy in Nigeria: his job was going well and he was settled, but my mother was a strong woman and she convinced him to come over for two years. It was here that she gave birth to my sister, Catherine. A year later, she had my youngest sister, Sarah.

As far as my mother was concerned, she had put all thoughts of sickle cell from her mind. Then, when I was three, I suddenly started crying hysterically. She called the doctor to come to the house and have a look at me. He came immediately and advised I go to the hospital, so Mum took me to University College Hospital, where the doctors thought I might have appendicitis and wanted to operate. They decided against it, though, and merely managed my condition with painkillers.

It was at this point that a good friend of my mother,

Dr Biola, suggested to her that I might have sickle cell anaemia. She knew of this disease because she was a doctorate nurse and her husband a medical doctor. Determined to get to the bottom of the problem, my mum decided to have all her children's blood tested for haemoglobin S, which is the defective form of haemoglobin that underlies sickle cell anaemia.

She was very relieved when the results came back to show that none of us had inherited the SS blood type. I was shown to be a carrier – 'AS' – but I should not suffer from any of the incapacitating effects of the disease itself. Now that she had the confirmation she'd been hoping for from medical professionals my mother could relax, secure in the knowledge that her children were well, and concentrate on her teaching studies.

For a short while, all was calm in our household. I was a normal, happy little girl and my family were delighted that the previous symptoms of pain I'd experienced when I was younger no longer manifested.

Then my mother received some puzzling news from my nursery school – St Leonard's Nursery, now known as the Thomas Coram Centre, in Camden. They told her that I was eating foam, and they were worried about me. Greatly concerned, my mother consulted her doctor, and I was referred to Great Ormond Street hospital to see a psychologist who recommended I go for a blood test at the Hospital blood test department for them to better understand what was causing my unusual behaviour. This hospital had more advanced blood-testing capabilities, and when they had the results, the doctors called my mother for a consultation to discuss the fact that the test showed that I did indeed have sickle cell. This was a shock to my family as it was not what they were expecting. My mother was very confused as this meant she now had been given two different results from two hospitals. They repeated the test and again the result showed I had sickle cell and that the first test had been incorrect. My family was stunned.

The foam-eating apparently is not uncommon in sickle cell sufferers. It is a condition called 'pica', which is when a person has a craving to eat a substance that has no nutritional value – foam, chalk, coal – a little like a pregnancy craving. Apparently, this can help the sufferer deal with the pain, and to this day, when I am in pain or have had a stressful day, I like to eat a sponge!

Unfortunately, this news delayed my start in the reception class at primary school as the school claimed they did not have enough staff to manage my condition. This academic delay was something that would dog me throughout my school life.

Once my mum got past her initial shock at the diagnosis, she went through a series of emotions: guilt, anxiety and a terrible fear that her other children had also been misdiagnosed. I can only imagine her anxiety as she thought of the uncertain future ahead for me. But at this stage, while I was still very young, the full ramifications of the disease had yet to manifest, and much worse was to come as I got older and sickle cell really took hold.

MEMORIES

My first memory of having a crisis is from when I was about five. I vividly remember waking up in the middle of the night in excruciating pain. I didn't know what was wrong with me. I was confused. Was I dreaming? I cried out, 'I don't know what's wrong with me. Help me, help me.' I was crying uncontrollably and rolling on the floor in agony, desperately wishing for it to stop. I remember that pain like it was yesterday. My mother came rushing in and asked me what was wrong. She asked if I had fallen in school or if anyone had hurt me, to both questions I remember shouting, 'NO!' Bewildered and terrified, she immediately called an ambulance.

When I got to the hospital, I was given mild painkillers and told to rest, as the pain would go on its own. We went back home that very evening, even though I was still restless. My mother put me to bed and told me a story while I fell asleep. In the morning, as everyone was getting ready for school, I noticed a sharp pain in my leg which was getting progressively worse. It was time for me to have a bath and my brother came to wake me and found that I was crying with pain. He shouted to my mother who called the ambulance again to rush me back to the hospital.

By this point, my father had already returned to Nigeria to continue his job, which left my mum caring for all of us children on her own. And now, with her daughter in agony and without my father to support her, my poor mother felt confused and helpless. A feeling, I am sure, that many parents of children with sickle cell are all too familiar with.

At the hospital, I was given basic pain medication, which did nothing to help the relentless pain. My mother recalls screaming to doctors in the hospital, 'She is still in so much pain! How can you help my daughter?'

I imagine it is difficult to find the correct pain treatment for such a small child, and certainly at that time, when sickle cell was not as common in the UK as it is now, the doctors were still learning.

These bouts of extreme pain continued to cause me immense problems. I sometimes missed weeks of school and my mother's worries escalated. She cared for me around the clock as my appetite had ceased to such a degree that I basically had to be force-fed. Nights were especially difficult and the only way I could sleep was if my mother massaged my body to ease the pain. Even washing was a struggle because any contact with water sent shivers through my body and made me shudder.

It was only now that my mother began to realise the full extent of the devastation that sickle cell can have on the life of the sufferer, as well as on the lives of the sufferer's family, and she was in shock. She was also fearful of losing me, as the little she did know told her that sufferers had a reduced life expectancy. I can only imagine the strain she was under, caring for me, looking after her other children, studying, and also coming to terms with the reality of living with sickle cell. It's a wonder to me that she was able to keep going and keep studying despite her worries and the time she had to spend nursing me.

Unsurprisingly, she was overwhelmed, so she began to call friends and family to seek some comforting words and to help her digest the reality of the disease, and she discovered to her surprise that some of my cousins also had it.

But she needed more information. She had started to ask herself questions like: would I survive? Would I be able to have children? Would I live a normal life? She also wanted to know how to manage it and how to help me. But as this was the 1980s, these were questions that went unanswered, as little research had been done.

So she set out to educate herself and spent many hours in libraries reading up on my condition and discovering how best to keep me healthy. Below is a list of advice – both medical and practical – to try to keep a child suffering from sickle cell disease healthy.

CARING FOR A CHILD WITH SCD
- Fluids! Drinking plenty of water helps dilute the blood cells and consequently, hopefully, stave off a crisis. But be warned: all this water frequently leads to accidents. I wet the bed until I was thirteen because of the litres and litres of water I drank. Also, children

with sickle cell get more tired than other children, due to the lack of red blood cells, so they often sleep that much more deeply, which means they are less likely to wake up to go to the toilet.

- Rest. Children with sickle cell need far more rest than other children. Sometimes this can mean letting them sleep in and go to school late, or even skip a day altogether if they are too tired. This is very important because exhaustion can bring on a crisis.

- Avoid extreme temperatures. Children with sickle cell do not react well to extremes of temperature. So in England our house was always kept stiflingly warm, much to my sisters' annoyance at times. And going out was an exercise in dressing – vests, jumpers, tights, coats, scarves, hats... At the other extreme, heat can also trigger a crisis. Basically, a consistent body temperature is very important to maintaining health. This can make parents wary of letting children outside to play – this was certainly true in my case, which meant I missed out on a lot of play opportunities.

- A healthy, balanced diet. Obviously, this goes for all children, but children with sickle cell do tend to be thin and to grow at a slower pace because so much of their food goes to creating red blood cells. Don't worry, as long as the diet is healthy and all the food groups are there, this is entirely normal. (See also chapter 30 regarding nutrition.)

- Try to minimise stress. Anxiety and stress can be the catalyst for a crisis, so it's important to try to keep your child secure and happy. Obviously, this is what all parents desire, but there are small stresses that can be avoided:

- Don't ever force your child to do an activity or make them feel guilty for not wanting to do it. Feeling guilty for not fulfilling a parent's wishes will make a child anxious and may bring on a crisis.
- Never compare your child with others. Frequent absences and exhaustion will mean they may be behind other children academically and this will upset them. Try to encourage them to concentrate only on their own achievements, and not on anyone else's.
- Be patient and try not to show your anxiety to your child, particularly when they are ill. They will take their cue from you, and if you are panicking, or angry, they will become anxious.
- Try not to lose your temper with your child. If your child fears your reaction, it can cause them to become over-anxious about small misdemeanours – spilled drinks, messy rooms, forgotten homework – and this can bring on a crisis. Just to be clear, I'm not suggesting they can't be disciplined!
- You will know your child better than anyone else, and you will know what makes them anxious, so speak to the school to see if there are ways of minimising those problems there as well, particularly when it comes to tests and exams.
- Don't stress about their food. Forcing a sick child to eat when they have no appetite can not only make them anxious and unhappy, but worse, in the long-term they may come to associate food with anxiety, thereby creating a habit that is difficult to break. If their appetite is small, let them eat what they like

until they are better, even if it does seem bizarre. For me, I was obsessed with eating foam and chalk and refused to eat food. To get through my pain I would eat at least two large sponges a month. Even now, I crave that texture and feeling in my mouth. Whenever I have a stressful or painful day I love to treat myself to a snack on a sponge; it helps me relax!

CHAPTER 2

PRIMARY SCHOOL YEARS

As a small child, it was difficult to find a way out of pain because I did not understand what I was going through. I had to rely on others to remind me what I had to do in order to avoid having another round of sickle cell crisis. All I could focus on was just trying to get rid of the pain. I was only young, and it was difficult, and often annoying, to remember to keep drinking water, to keep taking medication and constantly feeling like the odd one out among my peers when all I wanted was to be as close to normal as possible.

When I started primary school at St George the Martyr in Holborn, to ensure that I stayed healthy as far as possible, my mother handed over a care plan to my teachers.

The school was instructed to permit me to drink water during lessons and have regular toilet breaks. I was very fussy about my food and would only eat certain things, so I took a packed lunch with me always, because I just couldn't eat the school meals that were provided. Whenever I was absent from school due to illness, the school would send me the work I had missed so that I could study at home. The teachers were also instructed to give me extra breaks whenever I felt tired or unwell. I was not allowed to participate in any sporting activities as this aggravated my illness. Although now, I think that sport is encouraged as far as possible for children, and this can only be a good thing. Anything that helps a child feel more included and less 'different' will help them.

All of these requirements were necessary, but even so, the special treatment left me feeling isolated. The other kids would call me teacher's pet, and there was a lot of jealousy among my peers, which led to my ever-growing feelings of insecurity, because I couldn't help believing that I was the problem.

But the concession that affected me the most was not participating in sporting activities. I didn't even learn basic swimming skills because of the risk of getting too cold.

The one time I tried swimming, when I was back in Nigeria living with my Aunty Okuwi, my mother's older sister, it was a traumatic experience. I was in my early teens and like many children that age I felt I knew best, so I went to the pool with my friends. Because I couldn't swim, I sat in the shallow end for about half an hour and when I got out, I immediately felt paralysed from the neck down. I couldn't even move to change into my normal clothes. The sickle cell pain was so excruciating that my hands and feet started swelling up. The hands and legs of SCD sufferers tend to swell a lot. This is caused by sickle-shaped red blood cells blocking blood flow to the hands and feet.

My cousins were frightened to see me in that much pain. Fortunately, they knew it was a sickle cell crisis and immediately they all got into their car and had me rushed to hospital. This incident left me with a deep fear of going swimming and meant that I never wanted to attempt it again. Sometimes I wonder what I would do if I ever had to swim for my life.

Luckily attitudes have moved on now, and the advice is that as long as a child is carefully monitored and not allowed to get cold, then swimming is perfectly fine. In fact, children with sickle cell are encouraged to join in with sports as much as they can, provided that they are supervised and monitored at all times – and, of course, not too tired. Which is good, because as I'm sure most people remember from when they were off games for any reason, that feeling of sitting on the sidelines watching as their friends had fun is isolating. That is what it is like for a child with sickle cell almost all the time – that was certainly my experience, and it was very upsetting when it happened.

Despite my mother's careful plans and the teachers' attempts to help me in primary school I suffered frequent crises in my childhood. My immune system was not strong. Also, my family was still in the process of learning the nuances of how my disease affected me both physically and emotionally.

The emotional stress is particularly difficult for any child. The fear of getting ill, the worry that friends will forget you when you're off school, the ever-present pressure of feeling 'different', all of this makes it hard to keep a child at school healthy.

When I was much younger, I asked if my friends could visit me when I was in hospital, but this changed as I got older, and I asked them to stay away. I was getting ill so frequently that it became difficult for them to come to the hospital every time to visit. Eventually, the visits dropped off, caused by a combination of the frequency of my hospitalisation, and the fact that when I was ill, I was just too tired to talk to my visitors and just wanted to rest.

In addition to this, when I was sick, I was often depressed – due to the painkillers, and also I found it difficult to come to terms with the fact that everyone else was having fun while I was always stuck in hospital. Of course, that's not how I feel now, but as a child it's so hard to be left out, and in the end it was easier if I didn't see anyone other than my family.

This caused other problems, though, as the worry of returning to school was then even worse. What if my friends no longer wanted to play with me? What if they found me boring because I couldn't do much? These thoughts can consume a child and cause depression, so it's important to always listen to your child and never belittle their anxieties.

I vividly recall a time at primary school, when a day trip had been arranged to visit the Natural History Museum in London. This would involve various outdoor activities. Everyone was so excited, and I so desperately wanted to go because I had never been on a school trip before. However, I was also terrified that I would get ill while I was there. In the end due to my anxiety my mother cancelled the trip and I stayed at home with her and watched movies and she took me to a local shop to buy treats. I remember this event so vividly because I really wanted to go that museum. I didn't understand completely why my mother stopped me from going; I was clearly getting myself very worked up. However, I would suggest if any parent finds themselves in a similar situation that it might be better to try to allay your child's anxieties first, even if this means a call to the museum or talking to the teacher.

STAYING FRIENDS

Friendship is everything for children, and yet with a debilitating condition like SCD, those friendships can be difficult to maintain. I think about my young self now and ache for her. It was so hard, and I firmly believe that teaching children as early as possible techniques to help deal with the emotional consequences of the disease is as important as the medical treatment.

If I could go back in time as an adult and do anything to make going back to school easier for that little girl in hospital who felt like an outcast, this is what I would suggest:

- Educate school friends and their parents about the condition by asking the teachers if you and/or your child can do a talk. This way, hopefully, the other children and parents will understand why their classmate has to have special treatment and not feel resentful.
- Try to encourage the teacher to be as normal as possible when a child returns to school and to assist in assimilating them into the class. It has been my experience that teachers were sometimes as uncertain as my classmates about how to treat me when I had been ill.
- Reduce anxiety by reassuring a child about anything that may cause worry and uncertainty. For example, if I had been told that though I couldn't do all the activities on the trip, there were some things I could be included in, it may have reduced my worry, and maybe, just maybe, I would have made the trip!
- Encourage your child to stay motivated and confident, as things will only get better. This can also be achieved by ensuring they take part in school activities. One of the activities that has no ill effects on a person with sickle cell is learning to cook. This is a simple, fun and exciting activity for a child with a chronic illness to take part in. It also has the added benefit of teaching them about nutrition and how to make healthy food that they like to eat.

CHAPTER 3

UNEXPECTED TRAGEDY

In 1987, when I was seven, we all moved back to Nigeria to live with my father who was living in Kano State while my mother moved to Wales to finish her degree. Looking back, moving to a country where healthcare is intrinsically poor and sickle cell sufferers have a low life expectancy seems like a slightly illogical decision, but my parents hoped that the warmer climate might help me cope better with my disease.

It was not easy, and something that was not taken into consideration was that extreme heat could affect me as negatively as extreme cold. This heat often sent me into a spiral of sickle cell crisis. We lived in the government reserved area (GRA) in Bompai Kano in a nice three-bedroom, detached house. My concerned father bought me an air-conditioning unit for my room, which helped manage the unbearable heat. However, the difference in temperature from the coldness of my room to the heat outside was too much for my body to handle.

Emotionally as well, I struggled to come to terms with living in a new country and starting in a different school. Although, on the plus side, as the food in Nigeria was all organic, my sickle crises reduced because what I ate and drank was very healthy for my system.

We went to Kano International School where the academic level was high. However, my siblings and I were bullied because of our background of previously living in the UK. But our stay in Kano State didn't last more than six months as my dad was asked to relocate to Bauchi State for work. I was starting to like my school by this time, and my father, understanding the pressure and how unhappy moving again made us, did everything in his power to make sure we were comfortable. He got a bigger house in a very nice area and we were enrolled at Bauchi Federal Government Primary School. Life went on as normal. As children, you learn to adapt fast without too much thought about what is or what might be.

At this point, my sickle cell pain was mild as my dad took really good care of me by ensuring I ate healthily, drank plenty of water and constantly monitored my temperature.

But then life changed significantly because of two major incidents. The first was by far the most terrible, and to this day it still affects my family, causing us all deep grief.

My brother Eric, who was two years older than me, suddenly fell ill. For the first couple of days, my dad did not think it was serious, but after a few days, as my brother's health continued to decline, it was decided he needed to go to the hospital. However the medical system in Bauchi State at that time was not good and the hospital performed invasive surgery that included an incision from his neck to the bottom of his tummy. I remember the scar this left as if it was yesterday. Unfortunately this caused an infection and Eric's health deteriorated even further. In a last attempt to heal him my father took him back to his home state of Anambra. This was the last time I saw my brother because, to our shock and utter anguish, he passed away.

It was a devastating blow to all of us in the family.

I particularly remember hearing someone ask my mother whether she wished it was me who had died, considering I was so sick from sickle cell. These words affected me greatly, and for my parents, too, who did not think of their children in this way, it was an incredibly insensitive comment. It certainly made me question my existence and wonder why I was spared and my brother wasn't. I was convinced for a while that the wrong child had died.

As I grew older, however, I tried to view it more positively. I tried to think that I had been spared for a reason and that one day I would discover this higher purpose. At the time, though, and still being so young, it was a heavy burden to bear to know that people thought that my life was not worth much.

Just a little while later while still living in Bauchi State, I suddenly started to understand that my ill health set me apart in some way and made me different from my sisters.

This happened when I came home from school one day with a swollen right arm. My dad asked what had happened, wondering if a teacher had smacked me – as they were allowed to do at the time in Nigeria – but I was a good girl and rarely got in trouble. In fact, there seemed to be no reason at all for the swelling, so my family hoped that it would go down in time.

After three days, I was still in a lot of pain and the swelling had not improved, and my father was frantic with worry. When you consider what he had just been through with the loss of his son, you can imagine his terror. He was convinced that I must have an infection that needed to be lanced. So he took matters into his own hands and, one night while I was sleeping, he used a razor to create small cuts on my wrist in the hope of expelling whatever infection was causing the swelling and pain. A parent will try anything to relieve their child and

44

my father, with no information or knowledge about sickle cell, honestly thought that what he was doing would help me.

I was so shocked when I woke up the next morning with five razor cuts on my wrist! Poor Dad – his drastic action had not helped at all, in fact, it had made matters worse. This incident is still vivid in my dad's memory. He gave me medications and I slept all day. But later that evening I cried out that my arm was still hurting. Having heard about what was happening, my mother told a friend and relative Professor Celina Okolo about my symptoms. Fortunately she was a doctor who lived in Plateau State working at the Jos University Teaching Hospital. She said that my father should bring me to her immediately because she was certain that I had developed dactylitis, which is a painful swelling of the hands or feet due to blocked blood flow.

The thought of leaving my sisters and driving over a hundred kilometres to Jos alone with me when I was in so much pain caused my father terrible anxiety. He recalls that he was so overwhelmed that he prayed to God and asked him for a sign that the journey to Jos would not be wasted and that I would recover. I can't even begin to imagine how my father felt at this moment. Having not long before undertaken another long journey with a sick child, only to have that end in tragedy, I can only think he must have been terrified that history would repeat itself. After he finished praying, my father said he was suddenly filled with hope that all would be well, and he drove me to Jos immediately. He remembers: 'I drove to Jos alone with Anne sleeping peacefully in the back of my vehicle. Surprisingly, the journey was very smooth, no stopping, and everything was all right until we arrived.'

As soon as we arrived at the hospital, Celina saw immediately that she had been right: I had developed dactylitis. This is a common problem for sickle cell sufferers, so parents need to be on the lookout for any unexplained swelling.

My father was told that he must leave me behind so Celina could take care of me until I was better, otherwise there was a risk I would lose my arm.

This was a painful decision for my father as he really wanted to bring me home to be with my sisters, but in the end I stayed with Professor Celina and her family for three weeks because the swelling was infected and I needed strong antibiotics administered four times a day via injection to help get rid of the infection. I was also put on intravenous fluid to get rid of the blockage.

My father was devastated to learn that I had been days away from having to have my hand amputated, and to this day, my right hand is very weak. Even writing causes me difficulty, and after a few lines my hand will go numb and floppy and I have to stop.

It was from this point on that I really understood that my illness would always set me apart and I was not as capable or strong as my sisters were and it really began to have a negative impact on my psyche. I felt as though I would never be able to succeed at anything, as my illness seemed to constantly hinder my efforts to lead a normal life. Even going to school sometimes felt like a challenge – the roads in Nigeria are rocky and poorly maintained, which made car journeys extremely uncomfortable on my fragile bones.

Countless times, my sisters would ask me to go and play with them and I would decline because I either felt too unwell or felt self-conscious about the various puncture marks on my arms left by the many intravenous drips I had. Kids are notoriously self-conscious about their appearance at the best of times, and I found it extremely traumatic to have my body pricked and poked with tubes and injections, so much so that even looking at these marks made me feel uneasy.

My sisters did their best to convince me otherwise, but I didn't listen. I wanted to be left alone. I was tired of not being able to do things that everyone else could and I felt like a failure. The realisation that I was so different and the stress and depression this caused me began to manifest itself in my sickle cell and I started to become ill more frequently, which meant that my studies suffered terribly as a result.

An important lesson for any parent of a chronically unwell child is to always be prepared for that rush to the hospital and have the patient's bags packed. I recall that my father would not be able to pack anything, such was the immediacy of the rush to the hospital to stabilise my condition. But not only this, you need to reassure your other children, as they will be very anxious as well. A good technique is to keep their minds busy. A disciplined schedule helps bridge that emotional uncertainty for other family members. In addition, allow them to see their sibling whenever possible. This will not only alleviate the sibling's concerns, but also give the sick child something to look forward to. For example, when I was in Jos, my father would always bring my sisters down every weekend to play with me. They would arrive on Saturday morning and then leave late on Sunday. These visits kept me going during that very difficult time.

CHAPTER 4

EARLY CHALLENGES

As already described, schooling was difficult for me through-out my childhood and teens. It's so hard for a child when they are treated differently to their peers. Missing out on activities and spending so much time in hospital affects your friend-ships, your education, your mood... It is all a challenge.

My early education was inevitably disrupted and incon-sistent; it felt like I was constantly playing catch-up and this became the recurring theme throughout my childhood and teens. When I was at primary school in the UK there was a better infrastructure in the education system so I was able to advance without significant disruption.

In Nigeria, however, the school was not as accommodat-ing. But even so, being schooled in Nigeria is something I look back on fondly. The hot climate seemed to favour my condi-tion, and Nigerian schools were very familiar with sickle cell sufferers and had a much better awareness of sickle cell disease than in the UK, which at least meant I didn't have to explain myself each time I was sick. Nigeria is, after all, the country with the highest rate of sickle cell births – approximately two per cent of all babies born each year. So the teachers were kind enough to understand the depth of my medical issues and were ready to exempt me from school sports, physical activities in general and the dreaded corporal punishment.

However, despite most being aware of the effects of this disease, there was a cultural issue that frequently came into play. In some communities, children with sickle cell were ostracised and accused of witchcraft of the worst kind. Little children were said to be possessed by the devil and were, in some cases, thrown out of their home by their own family. Parents in Nigeria have been known to abandon their sick children without any consideration for their future. As a result of these beliefs, I often came under attack from children who came from these backgrounds.

In addition to this, the concessions the school often made for my illness were not always well received by the other children and I was sometimes bullied for being different. For example, my abdomen was unusually large and I always had a yellow tint to my skin and my eyes. But worst of all was the fact that I was very small and very slim. My doctor had explained that it was very common for children with sickle cell to have slow growth, late onset of puberty and delayed periods for girls – mine did not start until I was eighteen – due to the fact that we do not have enough healthy red cells to provide our bodies with the oxygen and nutrition they need to develop at a normal rate, but this was of no comfort to me and made no difference to the children at school. For me it was just one more thing that made me feel isolated and hopeless.

Suffering from sickle cell disease also hindered my education substantially. I constantly needed to go to the toilet due to drinking copious amounts of water and I often fell asleep during my lessons because I was so fatigued. Also, throughout my childhood, I suffered many crises and this inevitably meant I fell behind and ended up being pushed back a few years, even below the grade of my younger sister, Catherine.

I can't describe how awful I found this. Of all the difficulties and traumas I suffered, this was by far the hardest to come to terms with. I loved my sisters, but I was the eldest. This position in the family hierarchy was important to me, because it was the only superiority I felt I had. And now even that was being ripped away from me.

Children faced with these educational delays and indignities can start to believe that they are a failure, so families need to try to find a way to minimise the effects. For me, the only way seemed to be by separating me as much as possible from my sisters within school.

Luckily, they have always been the most understanding and supportive people, even though they were young at this stage. My parents asked that I be put in a different class to them, so I did not feel I had to compete with them, and between the three of us we agreed that during break times we would stick to our own friends and keep separate, so at least I had the illusion of being in a different year to them.

But despite this, emotionally this was a painful period for me and it badly dented my self-esteem. Not only did I have my illness to deal with, I also had to make peace with the fact that I would always be behind everyone else and this made my feelings of isolation worse and I constantly felt I wasn't good enough. It was a problem that remained with me for many years, and only subsided once I had attained my university degree.

So, for much of my school life, I struggled with lagging behind others in my class despite the fact I was older than my classmates by two years or more. My sisters knew how depressed I could get about my failures at school so they began to develop innovative ways to teach me things they had learned in their respective classes as a way of making me feel that I was not missing out on anything. Despite being so young, they displayed an amazing amount of maturity to make me feel important and intelligent.

Since I could rarely play outside in the warm, enticing sunshine, Catherine and Sarah decided to invent games that we could all play indoors. They would write up mathematical equations for me in my room or formulate sentences in English and we would all sit and recite them together – and though it might not sound like a conventional way to have a good time, we had a lot of fun and it did wonders for my confidence. It was moments like these that made me realise that I was not as stupid as I thought because I would outperform my sisters in these games. I also realised I had a different way of looking at things, which meant I always had a solution for any problem.

Activities like these and the loving attention from my family helped me so much and instilled in me a renewed sense of self-confidence. I was able to feel and experience things like a normal child, even if it was only for brief intervals during the day, and it took my mind off my illness, which always lingered in the background, threatening to ruin my moments of fun.

Recently, I asked my sister what growing up with me was like for her, and she explained that for as long as she could remember she was always aware that I had sickle cell and she had to be careful not to do anything to upset me or cause me stress. This meant she and my other sister had to do all the chores around the house, while also looking after my every need. In addition, they were never able to plan anything for themselves because my health was so uncertain. She admitted that this did cause some feelings of resentment, but then every time another crisis hit me, they were reminded of how uncertain my life was, and how at any moment I could be taken away from them. So they decided that they must appreciate the time we had and never let themselves feel angry about any special treatment I received, or the things they missed out on due to my illness, because it was a small price to pay if it meant I would stay alive.

When she told me this, I was so moved to think of my two small sisters forced by circumstance to grow up too quickly and be selfless and loving when sometimes it must have been difficult for them. I wasn't really aware of how they were feeling at the time and how their childhoods were blighted by my illness as much as mine was, and yet they gave me their love so freely and generously. It is humbling to think of now. And it is the reason I have such a close bond with my sisters. They will always be my saviours, regardless of how old I am or how far apart we live in terms of geographical boundaries. They will always fight to lead me out of the dark tunnel of pain and suffering and help me find the hidden joy in life again.

BOOSTING SELF-CONFIDENCE

School plays such a large part in a child's life that it is essential for children at any age to maintain self-confidence. With the constant interruptions to schooling and the challenges this brings in terms of physical and mental recovery, it is easy for a child to feel like a failure. So for parents of children in this situation, I would recommend the following:

- Never compare your child to anyone else. Believe me, your child and the school will be doing this more than enough. It is a fatal affliction of our age, but at school it can seem worse, as all students are compared with their peers. Where do they stand in the class? What is the average mark for the year? How many people got an A? None of these are relevant for a child who struggles with a chronic illness and who is frequently absent.

- Ask the school to set realistic targets for your child and provide notes and homework for when they are off school to help them keep up.
- If your child has a particular talent or interest, ensure that there is plenty of time to explore this. This will boost their self-esteem enormously and also make them happy.
- If it is practicable, arrange extra help for the child. Some schools will provide this.
- Celebrate success – no matter what it is. As a child becomes older – particularly in their teens – this becomes more difficult because they have their own ideas about what success looks like, and it's usually got nothing to do with their own achievements, but even so, persist, encourage, praise and love. This is all you can do.

CHAPTER 5

FAMILY LIFE

I've already mentioned some of the things that can help your child through their early years and schooling. It's always so difficult for parents because they can see their child is suffering, and there are some consequences of this illness that are almost impossible to avoid. The emotional stress for one. Feelings of isolation and depression can descend on anyone following a serious illness, but for children with a chronic disease like sickle cell, as they grow, the realisation that their illness will always recur, and that there seems to be no hope of living differently, can be enormously damaging.

The temptation for any parent is to wrap their child in cotton wool to try to stop anything further from harming them. The impulse is natural, but even so it needs to be resisted, because when your child is well, they need to be able to live their lives as fully as possible. There may be activities that you are anxious about, but if you consult a doctor and they have no concerns, then you *must* let them do them. One of the most damaging aspects of illness on a child is social isolation, so I would advise always trying to make sure your child lives as normal a life as possible.

My father never saw me as different from his other

children – or if he did, he never let me feel it. I was so frequently sick that others saw me as a liability and a huge strain for my family, but for him, I was just Anne, his oldest daughter. He accepted everything about me: the difficulties of looking after me, the demands on his time, the extra expense of my medical care. There were times when he had to take me in the middle of the night to hospital – not easy in Nigeria where hospitals are usually shut at night – and yet he did it without complaining and treated me always with love.

My father tells me that only once did his fears for me overcome him. At the time he had been deeply impacted by the death from sickle cell of his friend's daughter – one of several people he'd known who'd died of the disease – and while he was driving me to hospital one day, his emotions overcame him and he had to stop at the side of the road, where he cried, asking God why he had to go through so much pain and suffering with me. But after a moment, he says, he calmed down. It was as if someone had told him to keep going, and all would be well.

One night when we were living in Calabar State and I was severely sick he refused to take me to hospital, because he was afraid of being attacked by armed robbers at night. I felt like I was about to die and I was screaming so loudly that a neighbour knocked on the door to see what was wrong. She said that she had a painkilling injection at her house and offered it to me. The injection stabilised my condition until the morning when my father could take me to the hospital.

The love from both my parents has always made me stronger and made me determined to carry on and prove to them their faith in me has not been misplaced. They taught my sisters to love me in the same way, whether I was sick or not. They all just wanted the best for me.

And this is so important for a child who can sometimes

feel they are a burden. Try hard not to be impatient when they are ill, and try not to show the difficulties that the illness places on you in practical terms, for example work and financial concerns.

However, for all his love and care of me, one thing my father refused to do was to talk about my disease, which I found confusing because when I was small, I could not understand why I was so different and what was wrong with me. This is stressful for anyone, let alone a sick child. So try to ensure that the child understands why they are sick and what treatment they will need. The more information you can give them, the less unexpected and stressful the next episode might be.

KEEPING THINGS NORMAL

As far as possible, try not to let sickle cell take over you or your family's lives. Here are just a few suggestions that might help.

- **Be prepared.** Always keep basic pain control available so if a crisis occurs then the pain can be treated until the patient can get to the hospital.

- **Let go sometimes.** Try to allow your child to live as normally as possible. This may mean allowing them to try activities or go to events that instinctively you would prefer they didn't. However, if you consult a doctor and they say they should be allowed to try, then let them.

- **Communication.** Talk to your child about their condition and the reasons for the restrictions on them and in return, *listen* to their objections. If the restriction you are enforcing – for example, perhaps with regard to a particular activity or social event – is more for your own peace of mind than your child's wellbeing, then be honest with yourself and see if there is a way you can reach a compromise.

- **Be positive.** Try always to present an optimistic face to your child. They will take their lead from you, and if you are wringing your hands and crying, they will feel there is no hope.
- **Take time for yourself.** Caring for a sick child is emotionally draining and stressful. Try to remember to take some time to rest or do something for yourself, especially when your child is well. This might mean trusting another family member or close friend to look after your children while you go away for a night. Don't feel guilty about this! Alternatively, don't give up on a sport or hobby that brings you happiness. It's easy to think you don't have time, but try to make time. For both you and your child's sake.
- **Don't be afraid to discipline them.** This is so important that I gave it its own section below.

HOW DO YOU TREAT SICK CHILDREN WHEN THEY MISBEHAVE?

I would always advise parents to, as far as possible, treat your sick child as you treat your other children with regards to discipline. You should be able to expect good behaviour from all your children, without exception, and the key is consistency. By this I mean being very fair and very consistent about which behaviours deserve punishment. The punishments may differ slightly – for example you would not send a child with sickle cell out to mow the lawn or wash the car – but the reasons for the punishments should be clear for everyone to understand. This is important for a number of reasons: the child with sickle cell will understand that their illness does not grant them special licence to behave badly or rudely – a very valuable life lesson. The healthy children will be reassured that they are all equal in their parents' eyes – this is often an issue for siblings of children who need a lot of care. It can feel like all the attention is centred on their sick brother or sister, which in turn can lead to attention-seeking behaviours on their part, or resentment towards their sibling because they always seem to get away with everything. Of course, this is a common complaint from all brothers and sisters, but if it is true, you need to address the issue.

This is something that my family did not enforce very strictly when I was younger. They were extremely protective of me and prioritised me for most things. They would always think ahead if we were going out and ask questions like, does Anne have what she needs? I was always treated differently from my sisters, which is sometimes hard for others to understand, because this disease isn't always evident and more often than not I looked well.

My father was always the backbone of our family and he was keen for everyone not to mention my illness or make a big deal out of it. He didn't like people to talk about or to me in terms of my illness. He tried, as far as possible, to treat me exactly the same as he treated my sisters and to make others do the same.

However, when I was small, I was not disciplined in the way my sisters and cousin were for fear of causing me anxiety. To be honest, though, I was a bit of a scaredy-cat and I hated being in trouble, so I was not very naughty. But there were no doubt times when I was moody and took my frustrations and depression out on other people.

Most people would forgive me instantly for any rudeness because they'd think that I had it tough enough already and they didn't want to add to my struggle. And for a long while my parents were the same. But as I got older, this lack of discipline affected the way I related to other people because no one ever told me that it was not an acceptable way to behave. My parents defended me within my family, but they could not defend me when I stepped into the real world. You cannot treat people rudely and get away without being disliked. This was a hard lesson for me to learn.

Eventually my parents realised that I could not be allowed to get away with things just because I was sick. And so they started to discipline me in ways that would not make me too stressed. Generally these punishments were small and exactly the type most parents use: taking away a favourite toy, sending me to bed early, cancelling a family outing.

But I vividly recall one occasion when my sisters and I behaved *very* badly. It makes me laugh now, but at the time, I could not believe we had been so naughty.

One day, I'm very ashamed to say, we stole some sweets from a local shop. I can't fathom what was going through our minds at the time, but children, as you know, are not always rational. Somehow my father found out and I have never seen him so furious. I know he was trying so hard to control his rage, because if he made me too scared he could trigger a sickle cell attack. And because he had to control himself with me, it of course meant he had to do the same with my sisters. So he sat us down and gave us the lecture of our lives. He pointed out all the reasons it was wrong and all the reasons it could have been dangerous for us. He made us feel terrible and very, very ashamed. Which is exactly how we should have felt.

However, such was his fury, that he couldn't leave it there. He wanted to punish us properly. So he set my sisters to work doing some heavy lifting of boxes. Obviously, he knew this was something I couldn't do, so he made me sit on my own for what felt like ages, while my sisters carried out all the tasks he wanted them to do. They didn't mind that I got to just sit there, because they knew I wasn't physically capable of helping, but the three of us understood that we had *all* been punished.

So my point is, if the three of us had all been healthy, it's likely that the punishment could have been far worse. But because he needed to be careful, he needed to ensure that we were all punished equally, even if those punishments had to take slightly different forms.

It's hard for parents to discipline a sick child, particularly if stress or anxiety makes them ill. And yet, aside from their illness, your child is just like all the others. They need to understand boundaries and they must never be given a sense of entitlement – by this I mean that they must never feel that their illness means that rules don't apply to them. Because if they grow up feeling they can get away with anything, they will come to grief as an adult, when suddenly the world around them is not as understanding.

CHAPTER 6

ON THE MOVE AGAIN

When I was eleven we moved again to Benue State to a town called Makurdi, as my dad's job required him to transfer to a different state every three years. This was a fun adventure for the family. Again my dad made every effort to ensure he found a good school and house for my sisters and I to live in. He enrolled us at Makurdi International School, which was the best at that time. It was a big primary school and I made a lot of friends there. Catherine and I were put in Year 4 while Sarah was in the year below us. I wasn't very smart so I was put in the lower Year 4 class while Catherine was put into the higher one. At the time, it didn't matter as we were never in competition with each other and also the other children weren't too inquisitive about my sister and I being in the same year.

The major adjustment for my father was in finding a suitable hospital for me when I got sick. Because of my sickle cell my parents were always very protective of me and didn't like me going out on my own. Looking back I see why, as due to the lack of great hospitals it was better not to be sick if you could avoid it. At the time, though, I would just get frustrated. To try to prove that I could do things by myself, I remember just after we had moved there, leaving the house to go and buy milk and bread. I knew I wasn't supposed to go on my own, but I was feeling mutinous.

I set out on our new bicycle and arrived at the shop with no problem. But after buying the bread, I saw there were three young boys about twelve to fifteen waiting outside the shop for me. Scared, I got on my bike and started cycling as fast as I could to get home. Unfortunately, as I wasn't very fit, I fell off just near my house and injured myself badly. The boys ran away and, despite the pain, I managed to pull myself up and walk the hundred yards home.

My father was frantic with worry, because we were still new to Benue State and he did not yet know where the best hospital was. Luckily, our neighbours saw my dad and were able to point him to the best hospital.

Apart from this incident, Benue was beautiful and you can see why it is called 'food basket of the nation', as many vegetables and exotic fruits are grown there. My family and I ate very healthily while we lived there.

Sadly, our primary school didn't have a secondary school attached to it, so when Catherine and I were ready to start secondary school my dad needed to think about where we could go.

This was a very difficult time in our lives. The death of my brother had affected my parents greatly, and my mother desperately wanted us to live in the UK: she was not prepared to sit back and watch another child of hers die due to poor medical care. My father, though, was not in agreement, but as my mother knew that one day we would come back, she thought it best that she stay in the UK. Inevitably, this separation caused the rift between my parents to widen to the extent that my father married again.

All of these changes and the continual moving around

affected us children greatly. Especially as my father's new wife was pregnant. So he decided that we would have a more stable environment if we lived with relatives in eastern Nigeria.

Catherine and I sat the exams for secondary school, which we both passed. I went to live with my mother's sister Aunty Okwui and her husband Edwin Onwusi in Enugu State to start secondary school, while Catherine went to a boarding school not far away because Aunty Okwui had five children – our beautiful cousins – already and didn't have enough room to take more than one of us. Sarah, meanwhile, stayed with my father for another year before joining Catherine at the boarding school. So for the first time in our lives, the three of us were separated.

This was hard for me, but the good thing was that I was not alone as I had my cousins to keep me company. Also, my aunty and uncle are the kindest people you will ever meet and did their best to adjust to my complicated demands: my strange eating habits, the fact that I still wet the bed, and the constant need to keep my room temperature regulated.

Unfortunately, the stress of leaving everyone behind and starting a new secondary school made me very ill. The school was much bigger than my primary schools and culturally it was very different as well. Everyone seemed more mature and very knowledgeable, and at first, the kids were not very friendly because I was different from them, but as time went on they became more comfortable with me and I made lots of friends.

Despite how kind and loving my aunty and her family were, I did not find the first months easy. My mother had explained my unusual behaviours to her, but even so, I was ashamed about some of it; in particular the bed-wetting. When I first arrived, I tried very hard to hide the fact that I had wet the bed, but by day three the mattress was too wet and I couldn't hide the problem anymore.

All of this made me feel very self-conscious and I started to become less confident, even though my cousins did not seem to care at all and never ever teased me. To try to stop myself wetting the bed, I started to cut down on the amount of water I drank, particularly from about four in the afternoon. And to my delight, it worked, but, unfortunately, it came with a much worse side effect – my sickle cell worsened to such an extent that my life became a nightmare. Everything made me sick – just looking at someone new could bring on a crisis! But I did not put two and two together. I was just happy I had stopped bed-wetting.

Things got so bad that one day on my way back from school, I fainted. Luckily, a neighbour saw me and took me home and told me to rest. But soon, I started to feel my sickle cell pain again. I was rushed to the hospital where the doctors told my family that my haemoglobin was so low that I could lose my life if I did not urgently have a blood transfusion. My aunty contacted my father who was incredibly anxious about this, as blood transfusions at the time in Nigeria could lead to more severe diseases if not done well. Luckily, my dad was a blood match for me, and so he rushed to Enugu to donate his blood. I reacted badly to this, though, and my entire body itched unbearably. But it settled after a while and I was sent home.

After a week, the pain came back with a vengeance. It had such a crippling effect on my psyche that I vividly remember each and every detail of that day. I was once again rushed to hospital and given a high dose of strong painkillers that made me feel strange and disoriented. My condition had deteriorated to such an extent that the oxygen was not reaching vital parts of my body, to the point where the doctors, once again, thought I wouldn't make it. I was in agony and just wanted the pain to disappear – I didn't care how. My family was called in and told that they had better say their goodbyes to me.

As I dozed in and out of consciousness, I, too, felt quite certain that I would not make it. I could hear my family around me, sobbing and whispering. I wanted to be with them intensely. But though I desperately tried to get up and approach them, my body simply would not allow it. I gathered enough courage to move a few inches, only to be hurled back onto the bed by the sheer intensity of my pain. After that, I remembered nothing.

I woke a week later, dazed and unsure about where I was and what had happened to me. I was told that due to the severity of my condition and the intensity of the pain, the doctors were forced to put me in an induced coma in order to allow my body to stabilise. My parents, aunty and her family and my sisters were all clinging on to me around my bed and I can still remember the look on their faces: utter relief and happiness that I was alive and back with them. As for me, I was just shocked to see all my family in one place!

It is moments like these that have given me an innate strength to carry on and fight, no matter how bad the pain is or how desperate I feel. I had had an intimate encounter with death and seen the effect that this would have on my family, but I had been given my life back. Maybe my father was right and I was, after all, as lucky as he believed; his own little Chiagoziem.

CHAPTER 7

TEEN ANGST

As I left my younger teens behind and started to reach the age of rebellion and wanting to go out with my new friends in Enugu, life became very difficult. As if missing out on education wasn't bad enough, what was almost worse, as far as I was concerned, was missing out on *life* – or so I saw it at the time. Sometimes the restrictions the disease placed on me, and the concern and care my family had for me, would get me down and I would feel stifled. I just wanted to go out and have fun like everyone else. Surely there was nothing wrong with that? If only everyone would stop fussing, then perhaps I'd be able to live like a normal teenager.

I would watch my school friends and simmer with jealousy. They could go to house parties, come back home on their own and go out to loads of other social events, while I wasn't allowed to do anything because of my illness, which also made me too uncool for other kids to want me around. It was so unfair!

This hugely affected my confidence, as I felt permanently excluded from the 'popular' group – the ones who were going out all the time. I felt frustrated, inadequate and desperately unhappy. I am certain that most teens who have been chronically unwell will have felt this. The teenage years are a time for spreading your wings and beginning to learn independence from your parents, but it was not my experience of that time, unfortunately. I knew the restrictions were there to protect me, but what teen cares about that? And I was no different from my peers.

I was so cross and unhappy that I stopped taking care of myself. I wanted to be able to eat whatever I wanted, like my friends could, and so I would eat junk food and drink fizzy drinks and try to pretend I was like everyone else. The result, of course, was that I had more sickle cell episodes, but I refused to believe that my behaviour was the reason for this.

Then one day I decided it was time I had more fun. Why should I sit at home when everyone else was enjoying themselves? So I asked my cousins if I could join them at a pool party at one of the hotels in Enugu. They were happy for me to come as they felt it would be good for me to get out of the house. I also invited some of the friends I'd made at school and my best friend Nennette, who was also a sickle cell sufferer. I loved hanging out with her as she gave me hope and we could talk about our pains and the methods we used to overcome them.

When we got there, we played tennis for an hour and a half. Unsurprisingly, we were absolutely useless, as we had never played before. And to make matters worse, during the game, I could feel pain coming on. However, determined to fit in and have a good time just like everyone else, I ignored it. But it got worse, and finally I couldn't ignore it any longer and left the tennis court to take some medicine, which I always carry with me in my bag. Afterwards, despite the growing pain, and still determined that I wouldn't let anyone else know how I was feeling, I joined the others in the pool. Because I couldn't swim I just stayed at the side of the pool in the water. The change in temperature made me worse. After ten minutes I noticed I couldn't move and the pain was so bad, I started to cry. But almost worse than the pain was the sheer embarrassment and humiliation. I kept asking myself why I didn't listen to my body and leave when the pain first started. When they got me out of the pool, I collapsed. Everyone came running over to me, and I managed to whisper, 'Please take me to the hospital.'

And so I learned that this was my negative reality. It was a harsh way to learn that if I didn't face the truth about my condition and the limitations it put on my life, then the consequences could be devastating. It is normal, when you are just trying to live your life like everyone else, to try to pretend that nothing is wrong, but if you do this, eventually, as happened to me, you end up cheating yourself from living your life fully and with joy.

It took me many years to understand that, though, and at the time, it made me desperately unhappy. It seemed so unfair that just as I had a little taste of how it felt to be a 'normal' teenager, I was so cruelly reminded that, for me, and for others like me, we have to find a different path to bring us happiness.

CHAPTER 8

HARD TIMES

Throughout these difficult teenage years, I was often lonely, particularly as my sisters were not at the same secondary school as me. But luckily once I settled in school and began to understand the culture of the East, things got easier and I started making friends. I picked my friends based on people who understood me and were not too crazy so I didn't have to do things that would make me sick. Which was why I always enjoyed hanging around with my friend Nennette and her family. They were my second family while I lived in Enugu. She always gave me hope and helped me when I was feeling down. Sometimes I couldn't understand why I was always sick and couldn't lead a normal life, but somehow, when I was around Nennette, everything was normal again. Even when we were sick we laughed about it, and when one of us came back to school after being ill, we would rush to be by each other's side to ensure we were not lonely. She was a shining light in my life at that time. She encouraged me to move back to the UK if I had the chance where I would be able to access better education and, even more importantly, better healthcare.

As it happened, my mother and Aunty Nkechi, another of my mother's older sisters, had already decided that my sisters, cousin and I should move back to the UK to live with our mothers. By this time my mother had gained her degree and was now a teacher in a primary school.

Unfortunately, before we could be accepted at a school in England our parents had to arrange for the three of us – my sister, cousin and me – to sit our GCSEs at the British Council in Enugu State. At this time of my life the fact that Catherine, my cousin and I were all in the same year, despite me being two years older, had really started to become annoying. However, my constant sickle cell crises meant that I was in no state of mind to study, and in addition, they had brought on a bout of anxiety that I was struggling to cope with.

As always, Nenette was encouraging and supportive. She even brought me back to her family's house to eat a special African meal called Abacha before the exams the following day. I sat those exams with a heavy heart. I was eighteen, the oldest person writing the exams, yet I was also woefully under-prepared. In fact, I knew nothing – and I mean nothing!

On the day of the exam, I went to the hall and when I saw the paper I was filled with dread because I knew I would fail. I wanted to run out immediately; there seemed no point in carrying on and getting an ungraded mark. But I didn't leave. Before we had gone into the hall my sister had told me to try my best, and I knew that if I left she would worry and be distracted and may not be able to do as well as I knew she could. So I stayed, and every time the invigilator came round I would pretend I was writing, but in fact, I left it entirely blank. Such was my lack of confidence and shame that I thought writing nothing would be better than writing all the wrong answers.

Towards the end, my sister finished her paper and looked over at me. She could tell I had a blank page in front of me and she was so upset for me. In fact, if she could, she would have written the exam all over again for me. Of course, that just wasn't possible. I was so tired and stressed by the experience that the next day I was in hospital with yet another severe crisis.

Sadly, even the most wonderful person can lose their patience, and by this time my constant illness was taking its toll on my aunty. It was easier for my mother and father who were not around to watch me day in and day out crying and wishing the pain would just go away. It got so bad, I remember, that after the exams, as Catherine was staying with us, she had to look after me in hospital because everybody else was fed up.

My aunty pulled herself together eventually and did her research to see what she could do to improve my health, and she found a doctor who made local medicine from native Nigerian plants. He made a very bitter mixture for me and advised me to change my diet completely and cut the amount of oil and carbohydrate I was eating. The drink was absolutely disgusting, but I was so ill that I was willing to try anything. I stuck religiously to the diet and within three weeks I started to feel well and strong again. This experience really changed me, and it was the first time I started to understand that health and diet go hand in hand – particularly when it comes to sickle cell sufferers. (See also Chapter 31.)

Before we left to go back to the UK, we returned to stay with my dad who was living in Calabar State. Catherine and Sarah left in August 1998 just in time to start school as they were both born in the UK and didn't have an issue with getting a visa. But I had to wait for the British Embassy to issue my visa, meaning yet another delay to my education, which left me feeling very down.

It was during this time while I was staying with my father that tragedy struck again. My mother called me at my father's house one morning to tell me that Nennette, my wonderful best friend, had died. She had had a severe crisis and despite the fact that she was always so careful, she had taken a turn for the worse and the doctors were unable to save her. The devastation I felt at her death is indescribable, especially as my sisters weren't there to comfort me. It took away a lot of my hope and I just did not want to imagine a world without my best friend. Many people told me afterwards that they thought I would be the one to die as I was always so ill, and I found it incredibly difficult to come to terms with the fact that she was the one to succumb to our terrible condition. Once again, I felt like the wrong person had died, and the guilt weighed heavily on me.

A week later I got the call to go to Lagos State to get my visa for the UK. This was another nightmare. Not only did this mean I would now be travelling to the UK on my own, but the sad news of my friend's loss had left me feeling very weak and I had not been able to eat. I became very ill in Lagos, but my father thought it best that I seek medical help there, and then board my flight as soon as I was stable, so I could arrive in the UK in time for Christmas.

This was a bad idea as although I was stable, I was still very unwell. So even though I managed to board the flight I was too sick to even get out of my seat. I remember the stewardess kept asking me if I was OK as I sat for the whole flight and didn't move, eat or drink. I also looked very unwell.

When we landed, there were two policemen and a doctor waiting for me. They took me to a room for an X-ray. I must confess I was too ill to even notice or wonder why the officers were there when I arrived. All I knew was that I was so tired and I just wanted to get out of the airport and home to my mother.

This was not to be. I was kept there for an hour and I was too ill to even remember what was asked. Looking back I now realise they probably thought I was a drug smuggler, which was why I didn't eat or drink anything! Finally, they let me go and see my mother and sisters who were waiting patiently for me.

This incident is a perfect illustration of why, when you are ill, you *must* let people know, otherwise it can be confused with something else and your treatment will be delayed. Who knows, you could even end up in prison!

CHAPTER 9

BACK IN THE UK

Being back with my mother and sisters again was wonderful, but I was really surprised to see where my mother was living. It was a very small house with just one bathroom and toilet. I hated it so much that I got depressed. Not only was the house very small, my mother did not drive so this meant I had to catch the bus. I hated this!

I also must confess that all those years of being away from my mother made it hard for her to know how to manage my illness. She loved me dearly but didn't realise I would be sick all the time and she wasn't prepared for the trouble this would bring to her life both at work and personally, especially when she also had my sisters to deal with. So although I was happy we were all together, it took me a good few months to get myself settled. This wasn't helped by the fact that my sickle cell did not improve at all. In fact it got worse.

Then came the ultimate humiliation. In all the upheaval of my last few weeks in Nigeria, and the death of my beloved Nennette, I had almost completely forgotten about my GCSEs. I had not even asked for the results. I was puzzled as to why I had not been enrolled at the same school as my sister, and when I asked, my mother finally plucked up the courage to tell me my results. Unsurprisingly, as I had left my paper blank, I was ungraded for all my subjects. This was one of the biggest humiliations I had ever suffered up to this point in my life – and I had suffered a few! Being in a class two years below my age, collapsing in front of a group of strangers I was desperate to impress, being bullied because of my stature and for being teacher's pet – all of this faded into insignificance in the face of what I thought of as my abject failure.

To make matters worse, my family had opened my results and knew them before I did. Which meant everybody knew how badly I had done. So, while my sister and cousin, who had both done very well, registered with the school, my poor mother had to start the process of looking for a school or college that would take me despite the fact I had no GCSEs and I would be starting late. In the end, I went to Stanmore College to retake my GCSEs, and though I was determined to do well this time, my state of mind meant that this was almost impossible for me.

Please don't misunderstand; it was lovely to be with my mother properly again, but this was a painful period in my life. I was struggling with my identity and firmly believed I was useless and would never amount to much. As far as I was concerned, I was just the sick sister who needed to be cared for. Not the clever one, the funny one, the sporty one… It felt as if my illness was all that identified me and this was hard to accept. Nennette's death had taken away all my hope that things could ever be different for me. I was still underperforming at school, trailing behind my sisters and cousin. And the incident at the tennis court had taught me that I couldn't fit in socially in the way most teenagers take for granted.

The stress of the move and the exams meant that once in the UK, I continued to struggle with crises and pain. I must confess, I couldn't find my way out of it. My constant illness was partly due to the cold weather, but a lot of it was because of my negative mindset. I just could not accept the reality of my situation, so I did not look after myself properly, and for a lot of the time I felt hopeless.

In addition, my poor mother was overwhelmed by my illness. Although she had been aware of how frequently I was ill in Nigeria, and had visited on many occasions, to live with it full-time was a huge challenge for her. Especially as, to be frank, living with me must have been a nightmare at that time. The constant pain I was in and the drugs I was taking affected me terribly and I suffered from horrible mood swings. It was also a challenge for her learning to live with my idiosyncrasies – for example my bedroom had to be just the right temperature, otherwise I couldn't sleep, which meant my mother was spending a lot more on heating the house than she normally would. Plus, I had strange eating habits, which made it hard for her to plan meals for the whole family.

Then there was the fact that she needed to pay attention to my sisters and factor in all of their activities as well. And because I was sick so often, she was finding it difficult to juggle her work commitments and being at the hospital with me. It must have been exhausting, but such was my own attitude to myself and to the world, that I never appreciated the sacrifices she was making for me – and in fact had been making for my entire life.

I think of that time now, and how she used to come to the hospital early in the morning before work to give me a bath, and then would be there straight afterwards to give me the food I liked, and I realise how hard it must have been. And I did not make her life easier because I point-blank refused to eat the hospital food so if my mother did not come with food twice a day, then I simply didn't eat. So there really was no respite for her, even when I was in hospital. And, above all this, she was living with the overriding fear that she would lose another child. When I think of how her life must have been, and the pressure she was under, I feel ashamed of my teenage self, but I also understand that at that point in my life, I was consumed by my own physical and mental pain; it was as if I was in a long, dark tunnel, and I could not find my way out.

To make matters worse for her, my mother had several friends who also had children with sickle cell, but none of them seemed to be ill as frequently as I was, so I imagine that between her job and looking after me and my sisters, my mother's life became quite isolated as she had no time for anything else.

Going to college was also difficult. I was ill so much, and there was very little understanding about my illness within the college, which meant there was no support for me. And because I was feeling so negative, it was hard for me to engage with the work. Consequently, I did not do that well in my retakes, although it was enough for me to be accepted at Harrow College to do my A levels.

For parents, I would say that the teenage years are probably the most challenging. Your child is pulling away from you, desperate to establish their own identity and be like all their friends. They want to experiment and have adventures, but the danger is that they lack the emotional maturity to understand that they cannot be careless of their health. They cannot stay out all night and eat junk food all the time without expecting to be ill. The likelihood is that once in a cycle of illness, it will be hard to stop it without a change of mindset.

I wish I had some wonderful tips on how to help your teen, but really, love and patience is the best I can come up with. Also, I would suggest that you try to encourage them not to compare themselves with their peers, and remind them that their achievements, however small in comparison to others of their own age, are actually incredible in the context of the challenges they face. Psychological therapy can also help, but this is something to discuss with the doctors. Plus, research every avenue of help and support that is available to your child both from the school and from the government.

FINDING MY FEET – FINALLY

Starting at a new school to study for my A levels was scary but also exciting. My mother had been doing her homework, and she found that the government had a scheme to help disabled children at school. This meant that I automatically received notes from any lessons that I missed due to illness, but best of all, we were given help to buy a car to get me to and from the college, and I also got a disability badge.

This made such a massive difference to me as it meant I could stay warm when I commuted – taking the bus had been making me sick – and also I could park right by the college so I didn't have to walk very far. Following such a difficult year, my health was even more fragile than usual, and even walking a short distance could make me ill.

These two changes in my life made me realise that with the right help, maybe I would be able to pass my exams, and perhaps even go to university. I started to look around for a university that would suit me. My mother wanted me to be able to live at home so she could ensure I was safe, so that narrowed the field down quite a bit. And in the end the university that stood out for me was the University of Hertfordshire. Upon visiting the University website, I determined that they promised a lot of support for students with disabilities.

When I called to explain my situation, the lady on the phone was the nicest person I had talked to in a long time; in fact, I believe she was an angel. She was certainly *my* angel at that time. She invited me to come to the university open day where I could meet other people in a similar situation to me and also discuss with them how they could help. I was so used to struggling on my own that this was music to my ears.

At the open day, I not only toured the campus and looked at the accommodations, but I also met staff and students from the course I was looking to study – Accounting and Finance – and, more importantly, I met the disability coordinator who explained how the university could help me. I was astonished and delighted. How I could have done with this sort of help at school! It truly was a magical day for me as I began to see that perhaps I *could* realise my dreams – sickle cell or no sickle cell.

For the first time, I now had a firm goal in mind, and as a consequence, I worked much harder, determined to focus all my energy on gaining my A levels. Unfortunately, at the same time as trying to do well in my exams, I still wanted to live like a normal teenager: I wanted to go out, see my friends, enjoy life more, so I had not changed my attitude completely!

Working hard and attempting to have a social life did take my mind off my disease from time to time. However, my mother was worried about the stress I was putting myself under, and she was right. Inevitably I ended up in hospital on a regular basis because of my stress levels and because I just wasn't listening to my body. I wasn't resting as much as I should, nor eating properly. The desperate desire to fit in and be like everyone else had not left me, even though by this time I was twenty-two – an adult. But because I had lived such a sheltered life and spent so much time being sick, I was very naïve and emotionally immature.

By the time the exams schedule came around, the stress created a chain of crises and I had to take some of them in hospital with an invigilator by my side. I had a crisis the day before and was on strong painkillers, which made me sleepy, so the extra time I had been granted didn't really help me much.

On the day of my A level results I was so worried that I would not achieve the grades I needed. My sister came with me, and I was overjoyed to discover that I had done enough! I rang the university immediately and accepted the place.

This was a huge turning point in my life. I was overcome with happiness and excitement and my family were so delighted for me. I finally felt that maybe, just maybe, I could achieve my dreams of a successful career and a loving family of my own. But on the back of this excitement, and after the years of academic struggle, I was suddenly engulfed with anxiety because I knew that the workload was going to be intense. However, I tried to prepare myself for it as best I could. This would be a brand-new start for me, meeting new people and having new experiences. I promised myself that I would not allow my previous feelings of inferiority get in the way of my ambition for myself or my loved ones, who were my pillar of strength.

I was absolutely determined to take on all the challenges and overcome any events that would try and stop me from graduating.

CHAPTER 10

HOW UNIVERSITY CHANGED MY LIFE

I was incredibly lucky in that the University of Hertfordshire had an intrinsic respect for people with disabilities. I did not expect them to be as understanding as they were. Of course, I had to make the professors aware of my condition and its seriousness, but they were kind and helpful in organising manageable parameters for me to work within and I was never made to feel as if I were a burden on the teachers. I was assigned a disability officer, who went a long way towards helping me get through the course. For example, if I missed a lecture due to a crisis, my disability officer would organise notes for me. If I was in hospital, she would coordinate with the relevant departments to make them aware of my situation, so that it would not impact my studies. Even if I had a single day clouded with fatigue, she would be there for me to provide all the moral and physical support that I needed. It was simply incredible and I feel truly blessed to have had her support, especially when I was down and out. I'm not sure I could have achieved the result I did without her. Having the support took so much stress and anxiety away from me and helped me see a way out of my burning tunnel.

I wanted to have a successful career and a loving, caring

family of my own, but I also knew I needed to take baby steps to build up the courage to do that. I realised I had to weave a mental path for myself and devise a way out of pain – a plan that allowed me to step away from the shackles of my disability and gain enough strength to try to accomplish what I had always wanted to do. It was primarily mental strength that I was looking for and I had to find that courage on my own.

I was lucky in that I had many people supporting me. My doctors wanted me to focus on finding a way to deal with the pain, so I could learn to work smarter – still working hard, but utilising my time in a better way, allowing me plenty of time to rest and look after myself. My father, whenever I called him to complain, would tell me over and over again, 'Anne, you can do it. You just have to believe in yourself.'

Whenever I grew weary or was bogged down by the intensity of my illness, I would remind myself of his inspirational words and feel better instantly. I wanted to succeed, not just for myself but also for my family who had done so much for me. They had given up a lot for me throughout their lives and constantly had to make allowances for my condition. Yet they never made me feel responsible for my illness or failures in any way. Their sacrifice for me is something I will cherish for the rest of my life. I wanted to show them that I was capable of accomplishing something that they could be proud of.

And so my education provided me with an outlet, something productive and separate from my disease, and the satisfaction I took from this encouraged me to develop the traits of tenacity and ambition as I grew older. And because I had to balance my workload with self-care, it made me increasingly diligent and productive as a student. I learned how to strike a proper balance between my studies and other priorities, including illness management. I had to learn when to allocate time for studies and when to switch off and take care of my physical health.

The main problem with SCD is its unpredictable nature, as you never know when you'll be screaming out in agony, and I continued to experience bouts of serious crisis, but even so, hope prevailed. Some of it was self-instilled while the rest of it was due to the external support provided to me.

Finally I had come to understand that, to become a better me, I had to accept help as well as not be afraid to ask for it. This is a realisation that all of us who live with a chronic illness need to come to. We cannot do it on our own, so accept the help offered, and it will make an enormous difference to your life.

I became very conscientious as I was aware that I had to be more diligent than most, as I was always at a higher risk of missing out on important course modules. I made sure I looked after myself, taking regular breaks to relax if I felt I was getting fatigued or unwell. I did not want anything to hurt my chances of doing well at the university, especially as they were making so much effort to support me.

It was in this phase of my life that I finally began to feel I was capable of attaining a fair amount of success. I do not mean that I wanted to be a success in the way others perceived it: I did not win any special award or anything like that. But I felt like a success because for the first time in my life, I was making progress, and it was all down to my own efforts. Plus, I was learning to manage my illness better and not allowing it to get the better of me. That in itself was a great victory for me. It might not appear something substantial to others, but for my family and me this was huge. And most important of all, I was finally understanding myself and finding my way out of pain.

PRACTICAL STEPS TO HELP YOU SUCCEED

For anyone in the same situation as me, I would urge you to make a list of things that work and don't work for you in your daily life. The university made me write a journal detailing, for example, why on a certain day I was not well, and what changes might have helped me to avoid the situation. I had never thought of doing this before, and it was incredibly useful. The following list contains the key points I discovered, and these helped me during my years at Hertfordshire:

- I needed to structure my calendar in such a way as to allow myself plenty of time to rest. Either I needed to be able to leave at lunchtime to rest, or I needed to start in the afternoon. I was lucky in that my course was able to accommodate these needs.

- I requested a Dictaphone because if the lecture was longer than an hour, I would struggle to keep going. This was enormously helpful!

- I made a note of places I could rest if needed – including the rooms of friends who lived in the halls of residence or nearby, so wherever I was, I knew there was a safe place for me to stop if I needed to.

- I explained my situation to the lecturers so they would understand if I fell asleep, or needed to leave for regular toilet breaks.

- I made sure that others in the class understood my situation so could help if I ever needed it during a lecture.

MANAGING STRESS AND ANXIETY

Enrolling at university helped me to develop new skills in order to balance academic demands with a healthy lifestyle. I was fortunate that the University of Hertfordshire was so supportive. It was here that I learned that stress is a part of everyday life and by learning to manage it, I would make a big improvement in my life. I was also made aware that we are sometimes responsible for bringing about much of our own stress, and once we can recognize how we do that, then we can practise specific stress-reduction strategies.

In my case, I knew I didn't respond well to competition as I felt I was always at a disadvantage. It did not matter what kind of competition it was – whether sport or education.

As I have already explained, for people with sickle cell disorder, stress can act as the catalyst that ignites a painful episode. But this does not mean that every time you are busy or face a difficult challenge you will become ill. I have noticed that not everyone with sickle cell responds the same way to potentially stressful circumstances. For example, if I knew I was sitting an exam with a family member – like I did with the GCSEs – who could share our results with our family, I got very anxious, while others are able to keep their stress under control.

For any of you who might be struggling with stress and anxiety in your life, and finding yourself trapped in a cycle of sickle cell crises because of it, I would recommend following these steps. These are the lessons I learned at university, and they are lessons that continue to help me today:

- **Take baby steps.** This was the key strategy in helping me attain my degree, and it is one I would urge anyone who has to contend with frequent interruptions to their work or educational schedule due to illness to adopt. I set myself smaller goals, which I was able to meet, and stopped comparing my abilities to others. Rather than think I could do everything, I became more realistic in my expectations and took into consideration any time I had lost through illness and accepted how this affected my performance. Setting the bar too high can discourage you, especially when sickle cell gets in the way of you achieving your goal. It can also discourage you from getting started in the first place. 'Baby steps' became my new phrase; I knew I was weak and tired but with baby steps I was able to keep moving forward. By doing a few things consistently and constantly, you will find you will be more productive than if you compile a massive to-do list, which, realistically, can never be completed.

- **Do not compare yourself to others**. I've said this before, but it's always worth repeating. Always remember that no one knows better than you the hell you are going through so comparing yourself to others will not help make your life any easier. It is better, instead, to focus on yourself and how you can move forward. For me, this entailed enrolling at a separate school away from my family and in a place where I could form my own identity. This helped me to truly find myself and take the blame for things I did wrong rather than pointing fingers at others or blaming my environment for my failures. I was able to stand up for what I believed in without my siblings feeling pity for me or trying to do things for me. With this newfound freedom, I was able to learn to understand my responsibilities, accomplish my goals and still have time for rest and relaxation.

- **Do not be afraid to ask for help**. On the whole, people are really very understanding if you reach out to them. I was lucky in that I found a university that did everything in their power to make my life easier and to take stress away from me, and it is thanks to that support that I managed to achieve my goal. Everyone needs help at some point in their lives, but when you are fighting a chronic illness, you need it that much more. Don't be ashamed to admit it. Because without practical support, you will struggle. Accepting that this is your reality, and being grateful for the help that you get, will allow you to relax and tackle your challenges with renewed energy.

- **Avoid procrastination.** With the help of friends and family, I learned how to avoid procrastination – like putting off assignments or responsibilities until the last minute. At university, I had a tutor who was there to remind me about my deadlines and who put me on a strict and realistic schedule. This was especially helpful for me when I returned from a week-long stay at the hospital.

- **Pace yourself.** I would take regular breaks from work or other structured activities throughout the day. During breaks from class, studying, or work, I spent my free time walking, listening to music or just sitting quietly to clear and calm my mind.

- **Recognise your own role in your stress.** Challenge beliefs you may hold about yourself and your situation that may not be accurate. For example, don't think you are a failure because you didn't perform well in a test, or couldn't fulfil a commitment due to illness. Instead, accept that it was out of your control, and take steps to get back on track. Whenever I think I am falling short of what I think I *should* be accomplishing, I seek the support of friends and family so I can vent about situations that bring on stressful feelings, rather than letting the negative thoughts go round and round in my head, whipping me into a state of anxiety.

- **Don't focus on the negative.** When you are feeling particularly down about your situation, try to think of at least three things that are going well for you, and share those experiences. Being aware or mindful allows you to focus on the events of the moment, and on caring for yourself now, rather than dwelling on past failures or anticipating what might happen in the future. When I was a student, I found that my life and my mind were often so busy that I forgot to take notice of the everyday occurrences that kept my senses 'awake', when these were the very things I needed to focus on to bring me back into the present and give me the strength to keep going.

- **Try not to miss out on fun.** When you have an illness you can easily forget to have fun, because you are so focused on getting your work done while also making sure you have time to rest. But rather than allowing yourself to miss the moment it is important to pause, take a breath and notice what you are experiencing. Your experiences may be pleasant and worth savouring. But even if they are unpleasant, you will be better able to cope if you face this directly.

  During my days at university, I missed so many great moments as I didn't want to be sick and never took the time out to socialise with friends or even enjoy being in a different environment or just being a student. So try to build in some time to enjoy yourself!

Thanks to the support I received and the lessons I learned about managing my stress, I graduated university with a 2:1. When I got the result, I was simply euphoric. For me this was not just a reflection of my academic ability, but also showed how far I had come in learning to cope with my illness. Finally, finally,

I was not just the sick daughter: poor Anne who needed so much care and support. I had a degree and I had prospects, and for the first time I knew that I could achieve whatever I set my mind to.

CHAPTER 11

BURNING AMBITIONS

After my success with my Bachelor's degree, I had a burning desire to do more. I wanted to keep on proving to myself and others that I could do anything that others could do, despite my disease. I'm not sure who I was trying to impress, to be honest, because nobody else cared!

I had begun to set my sights on a career in banking and wanted to give myself the best chance of achieving this. Everyone had told me that it would be difficult to break into banking and I should look at other options, but as a girl who was used to rejection and failure, I thought to myself, what was the worst that could happen? After studying at the university, I felt I could achieve anything, so I decided that, rather than go straight into a job, I would study for a Master's. I had managed my studies along with my illness pretty well during my degree, and it seemed like an obvious choice. So I applied to Cass Business School to do a one-year, full-time expertly structured Investment Management Postgraduate Programme. I believed if I was to make it into the City, a university in the heart of the City was a great starting point as there was a strong practical element to the course, which would teach me the link between theory and practice, and I needed to learn more about real-world accounting and finance if I wanted to have access to a wider range of rewarding international roles. As an ambitious student who had just recently graduated I was happy when I got the acceptance letter.

I did not expect it to be easy, and I was right! Despite all the lessons I had learned over the previous three years, during my Master's, the pressure of writing my dissertation really got to me and I fell unwell several times. In addition, I had fallen back into some bad habits. I was not eating properly, I had decided I hated water so wasn't drinking enough, and I was going out with friends after lectures, as well as working late into the night instead of resting and taking care of myself.

You could say I became the victim of my own success: I had started to believe I could achieve anything, so I took risks with my health. What I had decided to forget was that I *could* achieve anything, but not without looking after myself and taking my illness into account. It's a common problem for most people: you remember the success, but not necessarily the hard work that has to be maintained if you want to keep achieving.

I was privileged once again to be given a disability assistant who helped me manage my workload. She thoroughly understood the course material and knew exactly what I needed to do in order to write my dissertation and she helped me type and plan my schedule. Without her, I am not sure I would have managed. But even with her help, I realised about six months into the course that I had bitten off more than I could chew. I was still desperately trying to catch up on all the missed years of education, and I could not compete as I wanted to, and the more I tried, the worse my health became.

As a consequence of all of this, I had a breakdown in a lecture one morning. An ambulance was called and I was wheeled out of class in a wheelchair. I was utterly mortified!

And, even worse, I felt stupid for trying so hard to fit in that I had neglected myself. To this day I still hate talking about this incident. But it did teach me some valuable lessons – although, I thought I had already learned them!

This is what I learned that day:

- **Do not have unrealistic expectations of yourself.** I thought that I could do a Master's degree and also have a full and busy social life. I didn't want others to know about my condition, so to fit in, rather than rest, I would go out for coffee. Rather than eat healthily, I would grab a takeaway. Instead of water, I preferred Coke…really simple, everyday things that most students don't think twice about, but part of living the fullest life you can, despite your condition, is learning – and accepting – your limitations.

- **Accept the reality of your condition.** The reality for many of us with sickle cell, and any other chronic condition, is that we have to be careful of our health. It should always be your top priority, because if you are ill, you cannot live a full and joyful life, nor can you achieve your dreams.

- **Recognise your own role in your stress.** Yes, I learned this at university, but I clearly chose to forget it. But by trying to pretend that I was not ill, I caused myself enormous stress. And when I became ill, the stress I felt as I fell behind with my dissertation sent me into a downward spiral, resulting in my being taken out of the college in a wheelchair…

Becoming unwell again was a harsh reminder that my body was not able to cope with high stress levels. It also meant that I had to take a step back and regroup; I did not want to get into a cycle of frequent crises and not be able to finish my course.

Just the thought of my illness plaguing my studies would make me petrified and unsure about the future. And inevitably that anxiety would frequently lead me into pain! So I took a month off from my studies to get well.

Sometimes it was hard not to dwell on the negatives in my life, in particular about how serious my illness was, and how it had plagued my well-being and emotional development since I was a child. When you're ill, it's hard not to let self-pitying thoughts overwhelm you, and I really had to struggle not to go back to those tumultuous times of my teens and to remain focused on the positive.

Somehow, with the help of my disability supporter, I managed to persevere through my sickness. I kept telling myself that coming so far and then giving up was not what my parents had taught me. I did not want to let them down. I constantly reminded myself of how much stronger I had become and that I would not allow sickle cell to dictate the choices I would make in life.

From then on, I redoubled my efforts to manage my stress levels and take care of myself. To do this, I had to make sure my dissertation did not overwhelm me. This wasn't easy, but I kept moving forward, working not only hard, but smart, so I could rest as and when I needed to.

And all my efforts paid off! I passed my Master's in Investment Management with merit. My previous failures at education were now a thing of the distant past and I beamed with joy for the entire day when I graduated. I felt like a real winner. Even now when I steal a glimpse at my graduation photos, I feel proud of my accomplishments, and it motivates me to look beyond my illness and strive to attain something higher, something bigger and something more purposeful in life.

After all the difficulties I had had at school and the

feelings of inadequacy that had dogged me as a teenager, finding something I could put my heart and soul into and succeed at changed my life.

But the biggest lesson I've learned is that if you're struggling with an illness, especially a chronic illness, you must try to prevent it from consuming you or demoralising you. Feeling weak and disempowered is worse than the actual physical anguish associated with these bouts of illness. And feeling powerless frequently leads to defeat. And I was – and am – determined that I will not be defeated.

CHAPTER 12

WORKING WITH SICKLE CELL

My Master's took me longer than it should have to complete because of my illness, and so while most of my classmates had graduated and moved on to work in the normal fashion, I still had to complete my dissertation, but I also needed to find a job.

This was both a scary and exciting thought for me. I had never worked when I was a teenager because my family had wanted me to concentrate on my schoolwork. Both my sisters had had jobs, though, and I had always been envious of that. One worked in the supermarket while the other worked in a retail store. My sisters, as I mention so often, were incredibly supportive, and they shared everything with me. They shared the money they made, the clothes they bought and all of their experiences. They never wanted me to feel left out, and these gestures meant the world to me. But even so, I could see how much working benefited them. They were learning so much and becoming so responsible and grown up that I couldn't help but feel left behind.

So by the time I came to look for a job, the only work experience I'd had was not something you'd boast about on your CV. One summer holiday while I was at university,

I managed to get a job in an accounting firm to do filing and data entry. I didn't tell them about my condition because I didn't want them to be put off, which I soon realised was a huge mistake.

When I arrived on my first day, they had prepared a very long to-do list for me. The first task was to file a lot of documents. Unfortunately, the files were piled on the floor, requiring me to bend and stand several times. Nevertheless, I got started. It didn't take long before I was very tired, but I carried on regardless. When I had finished, I was sent down to the archive room to bring up more files. After all the bending and standing, walking up and down the stairs was torture!

By the end of the day I was exhausted and starting to feel ill. And by the following morning I was in hospital with a severe sickle cell attack, and my mother had to call them to say I would not be coming back. She was furious with me for not listening to her, and I had found the whole experience to be so traumatic that it was something I didn't want to repeat anytime soon.

But by the time my Master's was coming to an end, I needed to put those sorts of experiences behind me. I was still determined to work in banking, but I was unsure how I would manage to cope in such a stressful environment – that is if I could find a company willing to take on someone like me.

This is a continual worry for people with sickle cell – or indeed any condition that might mean needing to take a lot of time off sick. But as luck would have it, a ten-week banking internship at any one of the five major banks, specifically targeted at people with disabilities and/or people from an ethnic background, was advertised at the school. Obviously the banks were keen to increase diversity in the workforce, and this sort of initiative is practised even more widely now, which is very encouraging for people with a condition like mine, although there is still a lot that needs to be done.

I couldn't believe my luck, and I set about making my application as perfect as it could be. I have always suffered from mild obsessive-compulsive disorder (OCD), and it really kicked in while I was writing my application. I spent weeks perfecting it because I felt this was my only hope of gaining a foot in the door. Once I'd pressed the send button, I tried very hard to stay positive. There was no point in stressing about what would happen while it was out of my control, and I knew I needed to focus my energy on staying well.

Three weeks later, I was invited to an interview! Again, I prepared like a maniac and tried to stay focused and positive. This was such a huge opportunity for me that I couldn't risk ruining it by allowing even the slightest doubt into my mind. When I arrived for my interview, there were a lot of other applicants, many with very visible physical disabilities, whereas I looked, as I always did, as if there was nothing wrong with me at all. But the interviewers were very understanding and interested in my condition, and by the end I had a very good feeling about it.

When I got a call offering me the internship, I literally fell to my knees. I was so grateful for this opportunity and so relieved that my focus and hard work had paid off. This was a powerful demonstration for me that self-doubt can be the one thing that holds you back. No matter what you are fighting against, keep believing and working towards your goal one small step at a time.

Unfortunately, once I'd started work, yet again my enthusiasm overcame me and I ended up overdoing it. I was working at Lehman Brothers, and they had been so accommodating and helpful about my illness, but halfway through the internship my line manager changed, and I didn't really want my new manager to know that I might not be capable of working the hours that were expected. So I pushed and pushed myself until I made myself sick. In fact, I fainted at work, and once again an ambulance had to be called. You'd have thought I'd have learned that particular lesson by now!

When I returned to work, the ten weeks were nearly over, and I was certain I would not get a full-time contract. But to my surprise my manager was extremely understanding and kind. However, I knew I could not rely on this to get a job. So I worked as hard as I could and got to know as many people as I could, using the power of networking. In the end, I was offered a job in asset management, and so my career in banking had begun.

GETTING THE MOST OUT OF YOUR JOB

For anyone entering the workplace there are some important lessons I learned while I was at the bank:

- **Be honest.** Never hide your condition. If you are honest about what you can and can't do, then you will not find yourself crushed under the weight of expectation, and your employer will not be unpleasantly surprised. Also, if you should be taken ill at work, you need your colleagues to know what to do, and to understand what might be wrong, so there really is no point in pretending to be someone you're not.

- **Use your time efficiently.** The key to success in any job is being able to deliver on your employer's expectations. However, for you personally, the key to leading a happy life is to stay healthy – and also to do well at work. So you need to balance these two elements in your life and try to keep them separate. It's the same 'work hard but smart' advice I learned at university. Remember that you may not have the advantage of being able to catch up on work after hours or at the weekend, so when you're at work, *work!*

- **Build in rest.** A full working day without rest is challenging for somebody with sickle cell. Rest is essential to keep us well, so ask if there is somewhere you can take a rest, and build in regular rest breaks throughout your day. This will help you work more efficiently.
- **Eat regularly.** When work is busy, and the day doesn't seem long enough to achieve all you need to do, many people just keep working right through lunch. But this is a terrible mistake. For most people, regular food is necessary, but for those of us with sickle cell or other chronic conditions it's *vital.* So, always make time to eat! Not only does it give you a break, it provides your body with the fuel it needs to stay healthy. One skipped meal could send you straight to hospital.

CHAPTER 13

THE DATING GAME

Marriage is something most girls dream of, but when you have a chronic illness you just hope that one day you might meet someone who will accept you for you and not be impatient with your condition. I always knew I wanted to get married and have children but at the same time I was wary of what I would have to do or give up to achieve this dream. By this I mean I found it hard to believe someone else could love and care for me like my parents had done all these years. I asked myself, 'Could anyone else really love me enough to make the sacrifices that come with living with me and my sickle cell?'

Relationships and the people you surround yourself with are vital, especially when you suffer from a chronic illness. Your friends and family will see you through your good times and bad times. I really struggled as a teenager to find my own identity and tried hard to find my essence as a person when I was around other people. The painkillers I was on at times made it impossible for me to interact normally with people as they made me irritable and moody, which meant I could be a difficult person to spend time with. I would instantly be filled with regret when I behaved this way, thinking, 'Why did I do that?' I did not intend to be so rude. It takes a special kind of person to be around me and give me succour!

The emotional toll that this disease has on you can also make you prone to mood swings, which for anyone outside your family is difficult to understand. If you experience a sickle cell crisis, you go from looking absolutely normal to completely paralysed in a matter of moments; so you can go from being optimistic and jovial to feeling very low, because of sickle cell, in the blink of an eye. My sisters have always understood this, and it is because of this understanding that we share such a special bond.

Some people call these sickle cell lows 'depression'; however, I hate to use that word as it gives me yet another label and, frankly, sickle cell is enough. But the reality is my illness can make me a demanding and impatient person who wants everything now, because I don't know how long I've got left – people with sickle cell are known to have a shorter life span. In North America, studies have been done where the median life expectancy of a person with sickle cell is 42 years of age compared to average life expectancy which is close to 80 years of age. In developing countries, that age is dramatically reduced to teens or early adulthood. Although thanks to modern medicine, this is improving in the Western world.

For these reasons, even though I always dreamed of having a loving family of my own, it often felt impossible. I had a constant nagging feeling that because my life was not entirely normal, no one would be able to live with me.

When I was younger, relationships were so tough for me. I had grown up quite isolated and I did not hit puberty until I was about eighteen, which upset me and made my mother very worried. When we moved back to the UK, I had noticed that my body looked so different compared to other girls. I was still very thin, and I felt intimidated by their womanly curves, so I avoided going out in the evenings and curtailed my socialising. This, combined with my disease, prompted me to become quite introverted.

While most teenage girls would be out on dates with their boyfriends, or going to parties with their friends, I would either be at home recovering from a crisis or catching up on schoolwork that I'd missed. And when I tried to behave like a 'normal' girl, I almost always ended up being sick. This has been a recurring theme throughout my life, and one I think I have finally come to terms with.

My sisters were my pillars of strength throughout this really challenging time. They understood the difficulties I confronted and never rubbed our differences in my face. I loved sitting around with them, sharing my thoughts and aspirations for the future, but I envied their confidence and their ability to go out all the time.

That's not to say I didn't try to date. When I was about nineteen, I finally plucked up the courage to go on a date with a guy, and to my surprise, it wasn't too bad. We arranged a second date. Disaster! I had a full-blown sickle cell attack. I always have an inkling when I am about to get sick, and I could feel a familiar tingling in my leg while having dinner with him, but I just didn't know how to tell him that I needed to go home. When he invited me back to his parents' flat, I was completely taken aback: someone wanted to spend more time with me and get to know me? I always thought that no one would find me attractive because I felt as though my illness was written all over me so it would be the first thing people noticed about me.

Determined to have a good time, I ignored the signs and went back to his flat. But I began to feel worse and couldn't stop fidgeting. He kept asking me how I was, and I replied that I was completely fine. In reality, I was imploring my illness to go away. He left the room to get me some water and before I knew it I was almost lifeless, as the pain had become unbearable. I had no choice but to tell him. 'I have sickle cell anaemia,' I said. 'I need you to call my mum and call an ambulance right now.' Not only was I plagued with pain, but also riven with humiliation. Then I realised that I would have to call my mum myself because she had a rule about not going to a man's house until I was more responsible. In other words, we weren't allowed to date until we were twenty-one! I told her I was sick and going to my usual hospital. I also called another male friend, who, out of concern, offered to accompany me but I told him not to come. I didn't want his presence in the hospital, coupled with the stress of my mother's over-protectiveness, to exacerbate the situation.

My date tried calling me afterwards, but I was too embarrassed to return his calls and I never spoke to him again, which I feel bad about now. I at least owed him an explanation, but being so new to dating, the episode had crippled me with embarrassment. I just remember thinking that I'd never meet anyone, because who would want me, a sickly girl?

I was utterly unsure about how to deal with relationships, especially when I was sick or dealing with thoughts of getting sick. I always felt sorry for the person who would have to contend with it and couldn't imagine that anyone other than my family would have the patience. As I got older, I realised I had to think about it more clearly. Thanks to my time at university, my confidence had grown, and I had learned to look at my illness in a more positive light, but even so, I was still wary of forming a relationship with anyone.

Much of this was down to the fact that ever since I was a young child, I had been told that I needed to be careful about who I chose to spend my life with. This is because if my partner was a carrier of the sickle cell trait then my children might also be afflicted with this terrible disease. I did not want that to happen to my children. This was a major concern for me. People have often asked me whether, if I had fallen in love with a man who had the sickle cell trait, would I have married him? The answer is simple: No. I have lived with sickle cell all my life, and I know the toll it has taken on my family and me, of the sacrifices they have had to make and the sheer, unbearable physical torture that I have had to go through. I could never contemplate passing this to my children. And so, I decided that I would not allow myself ever to reach the point of falling in love with someone if they had the trait. Which meant being honest with a date as early as possible.

This meant that, though I did not have many dates, the ones I did have rarely turned into a second. People were often intimidated by what the disease would mean, but also, one of my questions would always be: Is there sickle cell in your family? This might seem tactless and even a little unnecessary so soon after meeting someone, but as I said above, I did not want to risk having to make a heart-breaking decision further down the line. And I *could not* allow myself to be responsible for passing this disease on to any children I might have.

TAKING A CHANCE ON LOVE

It should come as no surprise that every book has to have a love story behind it, and mine started with a very ordinary trip to Oxford Street that became the catalyst for fulfilling my dream of having a family and a partner who would accept me for who I am.

In the autumn of 2001, I was browsing through a record store when I noticed a very handsome man glancing my way. I continued to look through the stacks of CDs and thought nothing more, but before I left the store, he had the courage to come up and compliment me. There was an instant attraction.

However, I didn't want to give him my number because, well, he was a stranger, plus I was me, and like I've said, I was nervous about dating at this time. But then suddenly I felt this wave of confidence come over me, so I asked him for his number instead. I wasn't sure whether this would come to anything, but I figured that I now had a choice, and if I had second thoughts, I could just throw the piece of paper in the bin – the end.

Over the next few days I couldn't stop thinking about him and finally curiosity got the better of me and I took a chance and reached out, and we agreed to meet that weekend. I learned later that Marvin was in his car when I called, and he never answers the phone while driving, but this time he did. I asked him later why he did this, and he said he just felt at that moment that if he didn't answer the call, he would regret it for the rest of his life. Had he not picked up the call my story would be totally different from the one that is described in this book.

But the familiar paranoia about my condition plagued me and I was sceptical about forming an emotional attachment to him. My confidence was still quite low, and I battled with thoughts of ending the friendship so that I could save myself from any heartache. But he was so romantic and respectful on our date that I could not bring myself to end it. Also, I can't deny that deep down I knew that Marvin, being Caucasian, would not carry the sickle cell gene. Even though we had just met I knew instinctively that if he was a nice person this union might stand a chance in the future.

However, I worried about what his reaction to my illness might be and wondered if it would scupper any chance of us taking the relationship further. I cannot be spontaneous like other people, nor do exciting sports, which he clearly loved. I began to question if he would even want to be with someone who was so restricted. He was an adventurous Canadian who liked sporty vacations with outdoor activities such as swimming and cold, winter sports like skiing and ice hockey; I wondered if he would really want to be with a woman with whom he could share none of this.

On our third date, I mustered the courage to tell him about my condition. Instead of the rejection and disgust that I had anticipated, I was met with concern and curiosity. He had heard about the disease and knew it was genetic, but that was all he knew. He had never known a sufferer and therefore didn't know about how it might impact someone's life. We discussed my condition at length over the coming weeks, but I could not shake the feeling that he didn't know what he was letting himself in for.

However, the more I explained to him, the more questions he asked, and I started to believe that he really was invested in this relationship. One day, after questioning him on the subject, he looked at me and said, 'Anne, I have my own baggage. I have two children and have been divorced. We all have our liabilities. This is just a part of who you are.'

And he was right. Because as I got to know Marvin there was another aspect of his background that put a different kind of emotional pressure on me. Marvin had two daughters: Meagan and Sierra, who were seven and eight years old, and to be honest, as our relationship deepened to the point where I met his children, I wasn't sure how I would cope and I was concerned that the stress of getting to know his children might make me sick – what if they didn't like me? How would I cope with that?

The first time I went out with Meagan and Sierra by myself, I was not sure how my body would handle it. I can remember the day so clearly: Marvin had organised a car service to take us around to some of my favourite shopping sites. We went to Harrods, Selfridges and Oxford Street and enjoyed a really fun day out. When I got home, I thought this wasn't so bad. I coped, I didn't get sick. And I realised that life is all about pushing one's capacity to take on new challenges.

Now the girls are in their mid-twenties, fulfilling their own dreams and ambitions as an integral part of the family around us. Just today, as I am editing this book, I am enjoying a day out with Sierra in Los Angeles while Meagan is texting me from Toronto with the latest pictures of the puppy that she and her husband have adopted. If I hadn't taken that chance and pushed those boundaries, I would not know these two wonderful women and my life would be all the poorer for it.

But of course, at the time, I couldn't see into the future, and though our relationship was getting serious, I was still worried about Marvin seeing me unwell. Our relationship began to show signs of strain as I refused to stay out late on dates or stay over at his place. I was not ready to let him see that side of me and preferred to be in the comfort zone of my home with my mum and sisters. And besides, I had just started to make progress at university and was finally learning how to cope with my disease and I didn't want to jeopardise this.

I still recall the first time I was sick when we were together. We had been seeing each other for three months when I was hit with a crisis on a cold December evening. We were preparing a meal, when I suddenly noticed a shortness of breath and a sharp pain all over my body. For me this was very unusual as the attack came on so fast without any warning signs. I left what I was doing and quickly went to get my painkillers hoping that the pain would go away. But NO! It got worse and worse and worse. I called Marvin and told him I was in the worst pain of my life, please call the ambulance and my mother immediately. When the ambulance got to the house, I was finding it very difficult to breathe and could not even talk to tell him not to come with me, as he had not been officially introduced to my family.

Never having seen anyone in such pain before, he was so concerned and scared that he joined me in the ambulance. I was admitted and given a high dose of morphine. When my mother arrived, she was very surprised to see Marvin by my bedside, but as I was in a lot of pain, she focused on me and just thanked him for bringing me.

Marvin finally left knowing I was in good hands with my mum there. It wasn't until a week later that I realised I had not been in touch with him. I was terrified that he might have been put off by what he had seen, and I would never see him again. I needn't have worried. When I checked my phone, I was ecstatic to see that I had a number of missed calls from him. I finally spoke to him when I was a lot better. He said he had sensed I didn't want him to visit, which was sweet and perceptive of him – I really didn't! I assured him that I would get better soon and begged him to keep away from the hospital. It may sound strange, but my mother didn't know who he was and because of my African culture, I wanted to keep it that way. I did not want him to become integrated into my family until I was certain that he was here to stay and that we had a future together.

I was still keeping him away from the family by our third year, much to his annoyance. During this time, I had experienced several sickle cell attacks while I was with him and I always insisted on going to the hospital alone. The first time he saw me in hospital was enough and I didn't want to repeat that experience. But by the third year of being with him and always being unwell, I realised I was doing myself no favours by hiding it from him. Then one day, he remarked that I was the prettiest sick girl he had ever seen, and that gave me courage and hope for a future. It seemed he wasn't going anywhere and all my previous concerns about him seeing me sick seemed to fade away. When I opened up and let him in, I found that even when I was hooked up to a drip and draped in an oxygen mask, I felt more at ease with him. And, even better, it didn't seem to put him off me!

When my mother next saw him at the hospital and realised he was not a doctor but was, in fact, my partner, a look of shock flashed across her face. I couldn't help but laugh. While I felt giddy because of the severity of my illness, I also found the situation to be quite hilarious. However, I explained the depth of our relationship to her and she understood, even though she was anxious about it.

It was not that my mother never wanted me to have a relationship or to get married; it was just that she was concerned for me and wanted me to be in a relaxed partnership where my significant other could manage my illness and take proper care of me. I remember her saying, 'I don't want someone who can't look after you and will end up bringing me your dead body.' Such a typical mother!

I knew Marvin was not like this, but that doesn't mean he found it easy to get used to me. To be with me is to accept the fact that there must be compromise. I am unable to walk for long periods of time and any form of prolonged exercise or activity is almost out of the question, which makes it difficult if we want to go out and do fun things together. It's a constant struggle. Marvin has always been so caring when it comes to situations like this and I will always remember the day when he arranged a car service to drive me around central London so that I did not have to miss a much-anticipated outing with some old friends.

Finding a partner is never easy when you have a chronic illness. You need to be sure you are ready to spend time with the person for better or worse, and vice versa. What makes it so much more difficult for sickle cell sufferers is the fear of the unknown. By this I mean the fear of not knowing when you will be sick. This is very difficult for me to deal with, even now, as one day I am fine then the next, I might be sick and hospitalised. However, what this has taught me is that you need to take pleasure in each and every day, and if you are not comfortable with yourself, you will never be comfortable with anybody. When you are anxious and nervous thinking about a situation, it just makes that situation worse.

THE EARLY YEARS OF A RELATIONSHIP

For anyone suffering with sickle cell or any other chronic illness, I learned that after the pointless first few years of dating, and keeping Marvin away when I was at my sickest so he would not see me bedridden and in pain, that it is essential to be open and honest about your condition.

As you have seen, I have placed myself in a lot of trouble throughout my life because I wanted to be like everyone else and live life like they did. My advice to people in a similar situation is not to close yourself off from love because of fear. You should definitely explore possibilities but try to ensure that you do so with someone who is loving and caring. Never rush into anything, especially when you are living with a chronic illness that will never go away, because your partner will need to be patient and understanding. It is not something to be entered into lightly.

Finally, never let your illness define who you are and make you afraid to find someone special; start to love yourself and allow yourself to be loved by others.

CHAPTER 14

LOVE AND MARRIAGE

By the time Marvin and I had been together for almost six years I was growing impatient that he had not yet asked me to marry him. Especially as all our friends were married or getting married and having kids. Marvin had stuck by me through some very difficult periods of illness by then, and I had just started my internship and completed my Master's, and I felt very sure that I wanted to make a firm commitment to him. I have said before that I am an impatient person: I always want to seize the moment because I never know when a sickle cell crisis might ruin the day. Marvin, on the other hand, likes to do things at his own pace, and I was starting to get restless and worried that the day might never come.

Then in May 2006, he invited me on a business trip to Chicago and proposed to me on the 96th floor of the John Hancock building. I was elated. My previous fears of relationships and my illness being an impediment just seemed to vanish. After seeing myself as the girl no one wanted for so long, to have someone love me enough to want to marry me was a wonderful realisation.

When we got back to London, I shared the news with my family, who already knew and were very happy for me. Reality also kicked in as planning a wedding is never easy and this was always going to be challenging for me while also trying to juggle work. By this time, I had been given a full-time position, and I was aware that if I became ill and missed work, I would be putting pressure on other colleagues, and any good will towards me could fade very quickly. I was extremely conscious of my relationship with my colleagues because I never wanted my illness to interfere with my professional work. How would I fare with the added pressure of a wedding?

I began to worry that my body would succumb to a dreaded crisis and that my work would inexorably suffer. And, inevitably, despite doing everything I could to try to prevent it, I became very ill during the wedding preparations.

My future husband and my family were my biggest support throughout this stressful period. I was also lucky to have a close group of colleagues at work who understood what I was going through and, more importantly, understood my illness.

But despite all their wonderful support, everyone was convinced I wouldn't make it. Weddings are stressful in their own right and when you're prone to becoming unwell with alarming regularity, the stress can really take its toll on you. Marvin understood all of the issues and wanted to get a wedding planner to reduce the workload and pressure on me, but I had very fixed ideas about my wedding and didn't want anyone else getting involved.

My wedding vision was centred on being a princess and on celebrating the special day in grace and style with the people that I knew would be happy for Marvin and me.

In hindsight, my motivation for this theme was that I needed the fairy tale to come true. You see, after enduring the hardship of the disease and living my teen years as a survivor from Nigeria, getting married had a special meaning for me.

After all, it wasn't so very many years before that I had believed that finding love would not be possible for me. So it really was a dream come true.

This meant that the venue would be all-important. We visited many locations, but they did not have the feel I was searching for. Then my sister Sarah heard of a location sixty miles outside of London called Highclere Castle – this was some years before it became famous as the backdrop to *Downton Abbey*. The location just warmed my heart when I first saw it, nestled in the countryside with outstanding views of the area. Inside, the old-fashioned aristocratic style was quintessentially English, and I found it enchanting and, for me, the venue exuded happiness and style. Of course, English weather being what it is, it could also accommodate everyone if it were to rain. This turned out to be just as well as it poured with rain during our reception!

Most importantly for us, however, our wedding was a reason for Marvin's and my family and close friends to make the journey, many from far reaches of the globe, to share our special day and connect with each other once more.

While all this planning was going on, I knew that despite my illness, I had to be fit and healthy for the day. Some of the guests had booked flexible flights as they were convinced I wouldn't be well enough to turn up, and I was determined to prove them wrong. *Nothing* was going to stop me from feeling well on my wedding day. I kept thinking positively and telling myself that I would be fine on the day and things would go smoothly.

Understandably, Marvin was worried, but I told him, 'We have to do this, I can't let people down, but more importantly, I can't let myself down.' Being the kind and caring person that he is, he tried to reason with me. He told me that it would be fine if we cancelled the wedding, but I wasn't going to accept that at all.

One of the many problems with my illness, and one that bothers me greatly, is that recovery after a crisis always takes more than a week. Adequate pain control is very difficult to achieve during a crisis and this requires me having to take very high levels of narcotics in order to manage my pain. This can result in a temporary dependence on these medications and can lead to me exhibiting drug-seeking behaviours as in my mind I think I am still in pain or still hurting. For example, I can become very demanding and will aggressively complain about a need for my drugs to be given to me and request higher doses because I feel my pain is not going away. At my worst, I will get angry when the drug is withdrawn because the doctors feel – usually rightly – that I am recovering enough to stop the morphine; but for me, and for many like me, we feel right at that moment that we need the drug all the time to live. On top of which, the morphine can also impair me mentally by making my head feel fuzzy and making me drowsy. And, perhaps even worse for a bride, is the resultant constipation caused by the drugs. No bride wants a bloated tummy on her wedding day!

But despite the fact that I was ill during the planning, I was not as ill as I might once have been because I made a conscious effort to put some of the stress-managing tools I had learned at university into practice. Here's what I did:

- **Don't be overambitious.** By keeping my guest list small and restricted to those who knew me well, I took away the stress that I might have felt if I was having a large, typically Nigerian wedding with a lot of acquaintances who might not understand if the wedding couldn't go ahead.
- **Write down what failure means to you, and how you would deal with it.** I found this very helpful (I know, it sounds counterproductive, but bear with me). If you visualise the worst-case scenario, and also visualise

how you would handle it and how the future would be following that, then you might see that it will not be the end of the world. Life will go on, and you will get through it. Doing this helped reduce my anxiety. What's the worst that can happen, after all? I knew there was a ninety per cent chance I wouldn't be able to make the wedding, but I refused to let that worry me. I figured that even if I was too ill it wouldn't matter, because at least I had tried, and anyway, the important thing was that Marvin and I would get married one way or another.

- **Make time to take your mind off your worries.** For me, this meant taking lots of short walks with my sisters and paying attention to what was around me. By focusing on other, less stressful things, it helped take my mind off any problems and the possible consequences.

- **Believe you can succeed.** If you think all your efforts will lead to failure and there is nothing you can do to stop the pain, then you will stop trying so hard. I always made sure that I was using positive thinking to face my problems. Tell yourself that you will succeed, over and over again, even if, in the moment, you don't always believe it.

- **Focus on your spirituality.** My belief and trust in God is a fundamental part of my life, and praying helped me enormously. But whether you draw your strength from God, or other spiritual practices – like meditation – it's important to find your peaceful centre: the place where your mind can retreat, rest and regain its strength.

- **Eat healthily.** This really goes without saying, but don't allow yourself to fall into bad eating habits

– like snacking on junk food – because of lack of time. Physically, your body needs the right fuel, so make sure you build in the time to eat properly.

Of course, I didn't do everything all by myself. My family and Marvin were simply fantastic throughout the process. Marvin and I would sit together every night in our kitchen, planning our wedding and sharing the workload. Remembering those tender moments still puts a smile on my face and I truly believe that it was moments like these that gave me the strength to walk down the aisle without a glimpse of sickle cell to ruin my special day.

It was such a wonderful feeling, and to this day I still look back at my wedding pictures and give myself a pat, feeling really proud of my achievement. In fact, despite all the illness that had preceded it, I felt healthier than ever on the day and it was such a joy to see our families uniting from different corners of the world. I couldn't have asked for a more perfect day. And, not only did I now have a husband whom I loved completely, but I had also gained two beautiful children, as now my responsibility to Meagan and Sierra had changed and I was a stepmom! Though this was a little daunting, it brought another dimension to the day and added to my happiness.

My wedding was a huge milestone for me as I felt I had finally proved to myself that my illness would not always get the better of me and it reinforced my belief in the importance of winning the mental battle over your illness, as well as the physical.

From that day, I truly understood for the first time that I could be the master of my own mind. Yes, my disease would still come and hit me hard, but if I managed it well and didn't allow it to dent my hope and courage, then I could achieve almost anything I set my mind to. I never wanted to let it affect me as badly as it had when I was a child or a teenager. I learned how to preserve my energy and know that, even when I was tired, I needed to motivate myself to do things to the best of my ability and try not to be afraid of what would happen if I got a sickle cell attack.

In short, I started to take ownership of my emotions, my health and myself. But even though on that day I thought I had it all worked out, I'm sorry to tell you that I didn't. Not by a long way. But at least I was getting there.

CHAPTER 15

MAINTAINING A LOVING RELATIONSHIP

As I discovered, maintaining a relationship when suffering from a chronic illness takes a lot of courage, mutual understanding and support. Sustaining a relationship without the involvement of any illness is challenging enough on its own, but the complexities associated with an underlying debilitating illness only exacerbates the situation for the couple.

I am blessed to have an understanding, caring partner in Marvin, who not only empathises with me, but also makes all possible efforts to understand my illness. He has been my pillar of strength and an unstinting support throughout our time together and he has made me believe in the sacredness and longevity of relationships.

That being said, an illness like sickle cell can take a toll on even the strongest and best relationships. After all, at the start of a relationship, the person with the long-term ailment may be very well and may make every effort to only see the new person in their life when they are feeling well. (Don't forget, it took me almost three years before I would allow Marvin to even visit me in hospital!) The reality of seeing your partner sick can come as a shock and the physical and emotional challenges inherent in caring for them will be difficult to come to terms with.

In many cases, chronic illness can be a major deal-breaker, especially if the extent and nature of an illness is not discussed in its entirety as early as possible. If you leave it too long, it will be a shock for them; as if the person they had been falling for was someone else entirely.

Those who suffer from serious diseases often struggle to figure out the right time to tell their significant other about their ailment. Feelings of anxiety, worry, anguish and uncertainty engulf the sufferer because you never know how the other person will react. Will they be accommodating and accepting? Or will they be reticent and take a backseat, offering titbits of sympathy? Or will they run away altogether?

Regardless of how one's partner reacts, you don't want to wait indefinitely before sharing your illness. The right time is when you feel confident and safe enough to disclose your innermost secrets, but if you wait too long, you could put both of you into a heart-breaking position.

Once the relationship has become more established, there are still many, many obstacles to face because, as anyone who suffers regular and severe bouts of illness knows, it's not just your body that takes a battering. Aside from the sickness, the fluctuating emotions can be very difficult for even your family who have been with you all your life to cope with, let alone somebody who has only recently come into your life.

The role of family can be crucial here, because it is typically your immediate family that has seen you suffer, struggle and cope with this illness and in times of crisis, your partner will need them to help them through the difficulties, particularly when they are not yet completely familiar with how to care for you.

I have been a sufferer of sickle cell disease for as long as I can remember, and life has always been about struggling, coping and getting past one day to another. When Marvin entered my life, it took some time for him to understand the details of my disease. To his credit, he coped with the challenges better than I'd expected. For any partner whose significant other suffers from a long-term, chronic illness, coping with the accompanying emotional and psychological complexities can be challenging. As we both realised, it takes two to tango, even in the context of making the healthy partner cope with certain lifestyle changes.

It took us time to feel comfortable enough to discuss our concerns and plan a way forward, although Marvin was such a sweet and caring person that he never made me feel that my illness would ever get in the way of our precious relationship.

But you might find that your new partner needs a bit of time to come to terms with your condition. This is a massive commitment, and though it's hard for you, the life adjustment for your partner is a hundred times more drastic. Give them time if they need it; try not to push things and be open and ready to answer any questions honestly.

Aside from the physical and emotional aspects, there are also practical considerations to think about, particularly once you start living together. Things like your role within your family, education, finances, social life and job, which is why both partners must be on the same page and view the chronic illness in a similar light.

Without proper, long-term management of the illness to try to ensure the best health possible, the patient is bound to grapple with feelings of inadequacy, low self-esteem and despondency, particularly if they are unable to work, and they therefore feel like a burden – I have experienced all of these emotions at various stages in life. On the other hand, the carer has to contend with frustration, loneliness and juggling job and family, while also looking after their partner.

None of it is easy, but the most important thing for a couple is to ensure transparency and communication. Confronting chronic illness can impede or jeopardise any relationship, which is tragic because those who are closest to us are our greatest support. So always try to be honest with your partner about all aspects of your illness, big and small.

After my initial apprehension, I had to be brave enough to be able to discuss my illness with Marvin at length. It is very important to share any worries, concerns or fears to allow you both to come up with a practical way of doing things together while coping with the illness. While it is natural for the sufferer to feel anxious because of the inherently personal nature of certain illnesses, you've got to keep all channels of communication open. If you find it hard to talk it through with your partner, consider involving your family and friends to simplify the transition and calm your nerves.

Often, the difficulty for the caring partner is to navigate their way through the minefield of medical challenges and caring about them personally, without losing sight of the sufferer's heart. Remember, it is the heart and soul of a person that is most attractive and builds the foundation for any long-term relationship. As the healthy partner or spouse, you need to scratch beneath the surface and be in love with the person, and not focus too much on the disease or the patient's limitations – or how that limits your own life. Which means that anyone who gets involved with someone like me must really *want* to be with them, regardless of the changes and challenges this will bring to their lives.

Similarly, the sufferer must recognise that matters of the heart are just as important as bodily constraints. It was only when I met Marvin that I realised how much I had been missing out on by holding back from love and not being confident enough to let people into my life. Then again, I can't imagine anyone other than my husband whom I would have been willing to let down my guard for. Because it was he who encouraged me to look past my illness and look forward to a life as normal and romantic as possible.

But even during our first few years, I still felt uncertain at times. It was only after he proposed to me on that magical night that I began to feel more confident about our future – even though we had been together for six years!

KEEPING THE FLAME ALIVE

For your partner, there is a tendency to start associating the world of disease, hospital visits, medications etc with the person they have fallen in love with and want to spend the rest of their lives with, and that is not what you want! So make it a point to make time for each other as a couple where the focus is not on caregiving. It's imperative that you both try your best to lead as normal a life as possible. Yes, there will be moments when the intensity of the illness will get the better of you, but you've still got to make the effort to spend quality time as a couple to create that unbreakable bond while also sharing precious memories that last a lifetime.

The key for me is to be in the moment and enjoy every day to the fullest, making the most of whatever opportunities you are presented with. Don't let yourselves get bogged down with the illness, or let it stop you doing things when you are well. And don't let your partner wrap you in cotton wool, because this can lead to missed opportunities and resentment.

Life is short and unpredictable for all of us; but for those who of us who suffer from an illness like sickle cell, the stakes are even higher because we never know what the next day might hold. Therefore, enjoying every moment, whether this involves doing mundane activities such as shopping or decorating, or going on holiday, and doing everything with a sense of togetherness can help keep a relationship alive. 'Till death us do part' can indeed be a reality in a relationship that is based on the strong foundation of love, care and affection.

That being said, keeping a relationship strong and healthy is not always easy. I have felt the worry that Marvin might feel like my carer sometimes, and I never want that to be the case. Plus, I don't ever want him to feel that he can't share his own worries and troubles with me for fear of my illness. We are equal partners, and though my circumstances mean that at times he has to pick up the slack domestically or help me in ways he might not have had to if I was healthy, this goes both ways.

I would advise that there is only one way to make it work – honesty. Marvin and I have only grown stronger over time and that is because we have ensured our relationship is a free space to talk and share our concerns. There is no point in me trying to feign that I am well some days just to protect those around me, as it ultimately puts more pressure on me and eventually on the family. And if he, in turn, is struggling for whatever reason – the pressures of work or my illness or whatever it might be – he needs to be able to tell me so we can address it together. We are a partnership and we help each other. And together we can find a way through it.

TIPS FOR A HEALTHY RELATIONSHIP

- **Communication.** As it is for any relationship, honest communication is key, but especially so for a relationship that faces the strain of illness. Particularly when there are practical considerations that need to be addressed.
- **Make time for each other.** When you are well, make sure you enjoy every second you can together. Even

the mundane tasks. This will remind you both why you are together – it's not so they can care for you, it's because you love each other and enjoy each other's company.

- **Be strong for them too.** There can be a tendency for your partner to try to do everything for you, even when you are well. Caring can become a habit, just as being sick can. If you find your partner is falling into this habit, do something for them to show you are fine and capable – whether it's arranging a day out for the two of you, or even just cooking a meal for them. Something to remind them that you are also there to care for them.
- **Make arrangements to ensure they have help when you are ill.** The pressure of caring can be immense, and if you can call on others – such as your family – to help as well, then hopefully they will be able to get some time for themselves, even if it is only to go to work without worrying about you.
- **Enjoy yourselves.** Love is precious. Never take it for granted.

CHAPTER 16

HAVING BABIES

Before I begin this chapter, I want to briefly talk about the National Health Service (NHS) Sickle Cell and Thalassemia Screening Programme, which was set up as a consequence of a commitment in the NHS Plan in 2000.

All pregnant women in England are offered a blood test to find out if they carry a gene for thalassemia, and those at high risk of being a sickle cell carrier are also offered a test for sickle cell. If the mother is found to be a carrier, screening is also offered to the father.

This test should be offered before you're ten weeks pregnant. It's important the test is done early – if you find out you're a carrier, you and your partner will have the option of further tests to find out if your baby will be affected.

I was fortunate in choosing Marvin as a partner because, being Caucasian, there was almost no chance he was carrying the sickle cell trait. But even so, once our relationship became serious and we knew we wanted to be married and have children, Marvin took a screening test to confirm that the sickle cell gene would not be passed to our children.

I did the screening, which involves a blood test, when I was eight weeks pregnant because even though I already knew I had full-blown sickle cell disease and my child would definitely be a carrier of a blood disorder, I wanted to know for sure whether the baby would have the disease. If we had discovered he had, we would have had some choices to make, but thankfully, this was not something we had to contend with, so the screening gave me peace of mind that my child would never have to face the difficulties I had encountered throughout my life.

To be on the safe side, when Connor was born, he was offered the newborn screening for sickle cell just to make absolutely certain. This screening is an effective intervention which saves lives as the early detection of the disorders and prompt delivery of the correct medical care to prevent infections and sickle crises has improved the survival rate of babies born with sickle cell. The programme also identifies carriers. Compared to the 1980s when it took doctors so long to diagnose me, this has been a major advance, and the antenatal screening programmes are currently being rolled out across the UK. It has already had a huge impact on improving the detection of the condition, giving people informed choices in pregnancy, and also on driving improvements in the quality of care, which has resulted in extended life expectancy.

I want to thank Dr Allison Streetly OBE, who set up the programme from scratch to full implementation and was the Programme Director from 2002–2013. Thanks to her vision and commitment, the newborn screening programme has now been included in Public Health England's (PHE) rare disease registry, through which it has been shown that the programme is achieving the expected outcomes of improving survival and ongoing quality of life for babies born with the disease.

An enormous debt of gratitude is also owed to the Sickle Cell Society, which worked with Dr Streetly and other partners to make this a reality. I was lucky enough to be involved in the screening programme, having known about it during my tenure as the chairperson of the Sickle Cell Society. I want to also recognise the contribution made by the Archbishop of York, John Sentamu, who championed the idea and who chaired the programme from 2001 to 2013. Rolling out a programme like this involves many people with diverse back-grounds, professional specialities and interests, and he was instrumental in keeping everybody focused on what needed to be done, as well as fearless in holding people to account. His overriding argument was always that it is only ethical to deliver screening if it means that affected people can then access quality services.

Despite the improved screening and overall understanding and medical care, though, for many women who suffer from sickle cell, the decision to start a family is not as straightfor-ward as it might be for healthy women. It's a well-documented fact that pregnancy for us is a high-risk undertaking: there is an increased risk of maternal and foetal complications as well as heightened incidences of perinatal mortality, premature labour, foetal growth restriction, acute painful crises during pregnancy, early caesarean section, maternal mortality and an elevated risk of pre-eclampsia.

Despite these alarming facts, I was always desperate to have a family, even though I knew it might never come about. But after meeting and marrying Marvin, it all began to feel eminently possible. In fact, of the two of us, Marvin was by far the most anxious about it. Obviously, he was worried for my health, but he had faith that I could come through it. In fact, it was the future that concerned him the most. His major worry was how he would cope once the baby was here. If I was sick, who would look after the baby? I assured him that my family would help, and he would never be left to cope alone. Anyway,

I was not pregnant, so there was nothing to worry about yet.

However, I also had my share of anxious moments because I was not sure I could even get pregnant due to the fact that I have ovarian cysts. I had discovered by accident that I had these, having assumed my abdominal pain was sickle cell related and ignored it for far too long. Until one day when I was visiting friends in Nigeria, the pain got too much to bear. I should have listened properly to my body at that time, and understood this was unrelated to sickle cell pain, but it's a trap many of us fall into, and as such other health conditions can go unrecognised until it is too late.

But to my astonishment, after getting an ultrasound scan done on my ovaries to look at how big my cysts were getting, the nurse told me that I was pregnant! I was completely taken by surprise. I had never thought that becoming pregnant would be this easy, especially after everything that I had been through. I even took a few more pregnancy tests just to make sure they were right! There were mixed reactions from my family to the news: my sisters were happy, but my mother was worried and very scared. And considering all the dangers listed above, I can't blame her.

KEEPING BUSY WHILE PREGNANT

I was working full-time at Lehman Brothers at the time, but by the third month of my pregnancy I realised that this just wasn't going to be possible anymore. This was a chaotic time in the financial world as Lehman Brothers Bank had just gone bankrupt and pretty much all the staff were losing their jobs. Luckily, my division of asset management was not part of the debacle, but it was still a very stressful time as the team was in transition to a new company, Neuberger Berman. With reluctance, I had to accept that my banking role had become too difficult to continue because I could no longer work with the same intensity the banking world expects of a person – not because I didn't want to but because I physically couldn't. Yet I was not willing to stop being productive. I needed a new challenge that would be rewarding but would not put my health at risk.

I decided to join the Sickle Cell Society as a volunteer. To do this, I attended one of their annual general meetings with my sister Sarah, and I found it very insightful; I couldn't believe there was an organisation like this that focused on sickle cell. At the meeting I remember telling Sarah that I was going to become a part of this organisation and also, if I could, apply to become chairperson when the opportunity arose. My sister thought I was mad to consider this, but she understands my psyche, and she knew how eager I had always been to try to bring about change for sickle cell sufferers around the world.

After the meeting, I immediately applied and was accepted to become a board member. This was an excellent position for me as it presented me with a platform to learn of programmes already available and to work diligently to make improvements in them. A year later I was elected chairperson of the organisation and in this role I was able to expand the board to include patients, carers, doctors and corporations who could help bring about a change in the way sickle cell was presented to those who could help sufferers of the disease and, most importantly, stir them into action.

Some of our proud accomplishments were to further develop the screening progamme, and we successfully lobbied the NHS to incorporate sickle cell into the nursing programme. For this the Society worked on establishing a universal care protocol for sickle cell patients in hospitals across England. I was also able to engage the All-Party Parliamentary Group (APPG) and worked with a group of cross-party Members of Parliament and peers from the House of Lords to raise awareness of the condition in Parliament.

The result was the Department of Health and NHS professionals began to make a real effort to improve the standard of care for sickle cell patients. Still more needs to be done to tackle the stigma of having sickle cell and to improve the quality of life even further for sufferers, and the Sickle Cell Society continues to work tirelessly to bring this about. I was truly proud to have had the opportunity to be part of this wonderful organisation.

In addition to my new role, though, I needed to prepare for the baby. One of the worries was how we would cope when I was ill once the baby was born, so to relieve us both of this worry, we moved nearer to my mother, so that if there was ever a time I needed to be at the hospital, she could help out in any way we needed.

To begin with, it appeared as if all the worry about my health during pregnancy was unfounded because my pregnancy was perfect. In fact, my first and second trimesters were almost tranquil: no morning sickness, no overbearing cravings; it was almost too good to be true.

But as I got heavier, everything got harder. My body began to feel much weaker and I struggled to perform everyday tasks. And when I reached twenty-seven weeks, I realised that my body was unable to cope with the weight of two individuals.

After experiencing a brutal bout of sickle cell crisis one evening when I was about twenty-eight weeks pregnant, I found myself in the West Middlesex Hospital for nine days. I was devastated. As always when I am sick, it is a struggle to stay positive, but it was made so much worse because I was plagued with concerns about the safety of my baby. I was given routine doses of morphine and I underwent regular ultrasounds to make sure that my baby was not suffering. It was chilling to realise that my illness could be harming this precious little baby within me, but all the scans came back fairly well. The baby was doing just fine.

However, disaster loomed again just three days after I had finally been allowed home, and about ten weeks before my due date. Another crisis overpowered me, and although I pleaded with my family that it would pass, they insisted I go back to the hospital as I was in too much pain. Whilst trying to administer pain relief, the doctors had trouble finding my veins to do an intravenous injection. It seems I had become more ill than I thought and had to undergo a femoral line procedure. This procedure is when a line is inserted into the femoral artery at the top of the thigh so that they can administer pain relief and take blood for the daily blood test. And yes, it is as horrible and painful as it sounds!

The next few days were brutal, and I remained bedridden, writhing in pain. My anxieties for my baby escalated and I can still remember the way my heart thudded constantly with worry about his safety.

I was being monitored by haematology specialists, who noticed that my condition had begun to deteriorate. Consequently, I was moved to St Thomas's Hospital in central London, where they had one of only two blood transfusion machines in England at that time. This machine would take blood out and replace the blood in the same operation. By this time, I was less worried about my child as I was sedated so heavily, my mind was just a fog and to make matters worse, I also had an infection. Every medication that you are advised not to take while pregnant was administered to me.

After the blood transfusion I was more stable; however, the doctors noticed my baby's heart rate had begun to soar and would not slow down. I could hear the thudding of his heart on the scan and it sent shivers of distress down my spine. The doctor informed me that he would have to be born prematurely, five weeks ahead of the planned date. Despite the doctors' soothing words that my baby would be fine, I could not help but feel that my body had let him down. It was debilitating. But equally, I was relieved in another way, as it meant that at least my poor baby would be spared from having to take any more of the drugs I was being given.

Finally, on September 10th, 2009, I underwent a caesarean section with my family and Marvin firmly by my side and gave birth to a beautiful little boy, Connor Taylor Welsh. He had to be kept in hospital as he was not feeling very well and wasn't ready to feed on his own. This was fine by me as I wasn't ready to go home either and couldn't bear the thought of looking after him while I was very weak and fragile.

It was simultaneously one of the most miraculous times of my life, but also one of the most difficult. To know that I was the cause of my baby being born early and entering the world sooner than he should have was heart-wrenching – and yet, how could I not be happy that he was finally here? At least in hospital we could recover our strength together.

For the next two weeks there was a constant procession of people into the hospital to see me, and to help feed and change Connor while both of us got stronger so that we could return home. In many ways, it was a truly magical time, and despite my illness, I felt blessed that at last I had managed to fulfil my dream of having a child.

BEFORE YOU BECOME PREGNANT

Knowing if you and your partner could possibly create a sickle cell child is very important. Having screening done at this early stage in a relationship sounds difficult, and it is, but it is also an imperative. Without this knowledge a longer-term relationship is put in jeopardy and an informed decision on taking the risk that a child will be born with sickle cell is much greater.

LOOKING AFTER YOURSELF DURING PREGNANCY

For women in my situation, it's even more important to look after yourself when pregnant. Physically, pregnancy is challenging for most women, but doubly so for sickle cell sufferers, so my advice to you is:

- **Don't ignore problems.** It's so important not to ignore subtle changes that might indicate a medical problem – such as swelling, dark urine and loss of appetite.

- **Work closely with your doctor.** They are the people who will see you through, so follow their advice to the letter. If they tell you to stay in bed for a week to rest – then do it! No matter how inconvenient.

- **Take prescribed medication.** Being disciplined about taking your medicine will help achieve improvement in your well-being. Sometimes when the medication takes time to generate health benefits, it's hard to stick to the regime, but don't let yourself get lazy! It helps sometimes to be proactive and learn exactly why you need to take the drugs, so talk to your doctor about it if you're unsure.

- **Eat healthily.** I know it's obvious, but it's so important. However, if your appetite is flagging, then eat what your body craves. This is better than not eating at all.

- **Rest!** All pregnant women get tired, but people with sickle cell battle debilitating fatigue all the time, and pregnancy makes it worse. My key advice is if you need to sleep, sleep!

- **Drink plenty of fluids.** It is very important to keep hydrated. I routinely drink two litres of water a day but when you are pregnant you may need more.

- **Accept help.** Don't be too proud to allow people to do

things for you. You need to conserve your strength in order to grow the precious baby, so if your loved ones offer to pick up the slack, accept gratefully.

- **Weigh your treatment options.** It's more than likely that at some point during your pregnancy you will need to take some drugs that might have long-term side effects on the baby. For my son, the antibiotics I took when I was pregnant has caused tooth discolouration. But for other medicines, the side effects may be more severe. Above all, make sure you have all the information you need to make a decision that works for both of you.

CHAPTER 17

BRINGING UP BABY

After two weeks, I was ecstatic to take my little baby home. His arrival became the glue to keep us all together and Meagan and Sierra committed themselves to being role models for their new little brother.

As this was the first grandchild for my parents and first time my sisters became aunties it was a glorious moment for them. They were able to timeshare among their schedule to ensure someone was always around to be with the baby and me.

But despite our happiness, I could not stop worrying that he might one day be traumatised by my illness. I also knew that, no matter how much I wished it wasn't necessary, I had to put an infrastructure in place to make sure that whenever I was ill, I would always know that he was cared for. In fact, being in the hospital for so long while I had been pregnant had driven this home to me, and between myself, Marvin and my family, we put plans and procedures in place for taking care of the baby if I was ill, and also for helping me in those difficult early days with a new-born.

Luckily, because we now lived so close to my mother, it was decided that if I ever needed to go to hospital, she would look after the baby while either I took myself to the hospital, or Marvin took me.

Even so, it was difficult. The nights were the worst – as they are for any new parent! But night times are so important for my rest, and they are also the times I am most in danger of having a sickle cell attack. But as I wasn't working, I knew I had to find a way through them, because no matter how willing to help people were, they needed their rest too.

When Connor slept, I didn't try to rush about tidying things and cooking – all those domestic tasks that become so difficult when you have a new baby. Instead, I would sleep, and no matter how much needed doing, I was very strict with myself about this. And somehow, between us all, we muddled through.

The bond between a mother and her child is powerful and as he got bigger, I did not want my illness to disgust or worry my little boy, and so when he was older, he would accompany me to the hospital, as I wanted him to understand the nuances of my illness. I never wanted it to come as a shock to him. It was challenging to explain it to him, but children are amazing in that they are so accepting. For them, life just *is*, they have no concept of how things might be different and so they accept everything at face value. He was a curious little boy who found my various pipes and tubes in the hospital to be quite fascinating. I never want him to fear what could happen to me; I just want him to know that he is safe, regardless of where I am.

For anyone contemplating having a child, I would recommend the following to help get you through those first exhausting months:

- **Plan everything.** People with an illness like sickle cell do not have the luxury of assuming that every day will be the same as the one before. Before you give birth, distribute responsibility between all those who've offered to help, so everyone knows what to do if you need to go to hospital. For me this meant distributing responsibility around my family.

- **Take time off work.** Obviously, if you are able to stay healthy enough to work during pregnancy, then you will have maternity leave. But caring for a baby may take its toll on your health, so be prepared to take longer off if you need to. Don't force yourself to go back to work if you are not strong enough.
- **Get help.** This isn't always affordable for everyone, but even just for the first few weeks, if you can hire a cleaner to take care of the domestic chores, then this is one burden less that you have to worry about.
- **Ask for help if you need more.** The best of plans can come undone, and also, those who've offered can't be expected to be on call all the time – they need rest, or they have their own responsibilities to take care of. I also learned that if you are struggling, don't be afraid to ask somebody else for help.

CHAPTER 18

EXPANDING THE FAMILY AND IVF

When Connor was five, I decided I would like to have another child. I was not going to give up on my dream of having a little daughter. Unfortunately, this time it wasn't as easy for me to get pregnant. We tried for several years without success. I was told that when you're fighting a chronic illness, your reproductive system can become a fairly low priority for your body, which may need to pay more attention to vital organs like the heart, brain, kidneys and lungs, and less attention to the ovaries or uterus. So, eventually we decided to try IVF.

We started trying in 2014 but the process was too painful for me, so I was forced to stop further procedures. This was despite the fact that there was an embryo ready to implant in me. I had to be honest with myself – for the baby's sake as well as mine – and I knew that I just wasn't ready. I was weak and tired and didn't feel capable of carrying a baby.

Then in 2016, I decided to try again. By this time Connor was seven and I felt ready and healthy.

This was a terrifying decision for me because I was concerned that the hormones I would have to inject would affect me again. In addition I was concerned that this invasive treatment would exacerbate my condition, making me less able to look after my son. I also asked myself what effect would this have on Marvin? If I became very ill, he would bear the burden of looking after our son and me, and this was hard enough already. In addition, I had an added complication. Having had so many blood transfusions throughout my life, I had developed a condition called hyperhaemolysis, which is when your body rejects new blood. So even when my haemoglobin was very low, a blood transfusion was no longer a treatment option for me.

Despite all of this, I was determined to try; I so desperately wanted Connor to have a brother or sister and, personally, I just wasn't ready to give up my dreams of having a larger family. Marvin and I discussed all the implications, and though he was worried for me, he was also very supportive.

Before I started the treatment, I consulted my doctors. They were very cautious for a number of clinical reasons, but also because of how difficult my previous pregnancy had been. They put together a detailed monitoring plan so that my health was well known to the antenatal doctors and they could intervene quickly if needed.

Now that I had the go-ahead from my local doctors, I researched where to locate the best place in the world for IVF treatment – the clinic that would give me the highest chance of success. This turned out to be HRC Fertility Clinic in Newport Beach, California.

I was very nervous about doing the procedure in the USA. If something happened and extensive medical coverage was needed it would be an extremely large financial liability, because no company would insure me and my sickle cell. I could get cover for general illness, but in the event of a crisis I would not be covered. It was a risk that Marvin and I were prepared to take.

Also, as the clinic was not familiar with me, I was worried that they wouldn't be able to locate my veins for the egg collection. And sure enough, when it was time, the anaesthetist was unable to find a suitable vein for them to administer the anaesthetic into. After all this effort I was terrified the procedure would be abandoned, but thankfully the anaesthetist finally found a vein in my neck that was suitable.

After staying in the USA for three weeks, to my delight, I discovered the procedure was successful. I could hardly believe it! I knew that I had only had a slim chance of getting pregnant, and I felt truly blessed. What was almost more miraculous is that the treatment had not caused a sickle cell crisis. In fact, I stayed relatively healthy (for me), and I wonder whether this was down to my positive attitude.

For any other women who has a chronic illness thinking about going through a similar procedure I would advise the following:

- **Be prepared.** Before you even start the process make sure that you are ready physically, emotionally and financially so that you don't have to worry about these things once you get started.

- **Listen to the doctors.** Do *everything* they tell you, even if you don't want to.

- **Listen to your body.** Rest when you need to, eat healthily, and if you feel at all unwell, talk to the doctor immediately.

- **Try not to worry.** During my IVF treatment I refused to let anything bother me. I tried to stay relaxed and not worry about the outcome, because if I started worrying, chances are I would have worked myself up into a state. I also refused to worry about the pregnancy, because that would have led to worries about the baby's health and sent me into a spiral of anxiety. I took each day as it came and tried to keep my mind calm and present at all times.

- **Be prepared for any outcome.** Nothing is a guarantee in life, and this applies especially to IVF treatments. Do not go into the process thinking it will 100 per cent work. For patients without chronic diseases it is just better than an even chance of being successful and with a person that has sickle cell this can be reduced even further. Be prepared for a positive result but steady yourself emotionally for a just as likely negative outcome. When IVF is unsuccessful it can lead to further depression for the female sickle cell patient; therefore, mental preparation is required regardless of the outcome.

PREGNANCY SECOND TIME AROUND

While I was pregnant, my sisters threw me the most amazing baby shower party. It was a magical day, made even more special because I had been too ill to attend the previous baby shower they had arranged for me when I was pregnant with my son. Being surrounded by so much love and laughter that day helped me through all the trials that were to come.

I can't deny that my feelings around this pregnancy and Caroline's birth were different to those I had the first time around. Maybe it was because I was that much older; or perhaps because I knew this would be the last baby I would ever have; or even because of the difficulties in conceiving her. But whatever it was, I worried constantly. I worried that I was doing something wrong; worried that Caroline would suffer because of me; I was terrified that she wouldn't make it through; and then, once the doctors were ready to deliver her, I worried about how she would be when she was here. Perhaps this anxiety is why, although Connor's pregnancy was difficult, I was sicker the second time around.

My problems started earlier in this pregnancy than they had with Connor. First it was a terrible pain in the lower back at around fifteen weeks, which made moving and sitting difficult. Then, once painkillers had sorted all that out, by twenty weeks, I was itching horribly. After some blood tests, the doctors sorted that out too, but a week later I was hit with a sickle cell crisis and had to be admitted to hospital.

I realised while I was in hospital at this time, that silos within different departments still exist and I found that when I was in the haematology ward, I was treated for my sickle cell crisis, but when I was in the obstetrics ward the baby was the focus. Getting all medical specialties joined up was a challenge for the medical team. Luckily my amazing consultant, Professor Porter, and his team were able to coordinate all of the knowledge and treat both me and the baby throughout the pregnancy.

As my pregnancy progressed, I started to notice some changes such as decreased appetite, aggressive itchiness, jaundice, and really dark urine – which my doctors diagnosed as cholestasis and pruritus – swollen feet, and frequent sickle cell pains all over my body.

To add to my woes, the hyperhaemolysis made it impossible to receive blood even though my haemoglobin level was low and dropping every time I did a blood test. I became so ill that I had stopped going out, as I couldn't walk more than a hundred yards at a time.

My sickle cell got worse each day, and finally at thirty-five weeks the doctors had no option but to deliver, so I was given a plasma exchange (the best option available to me now that I couldn't have a transfusion), and Caroline was born by caesarean the following day.

Unfortunately, I was so ill that I was unaware of any of this and didn't see Caroline until two days after her birth. It was magical to be able to hold her at last, but, like her brother, she was also having trouble feeding, so needed to stay in hospital with me.

This whole experience changed me from within and gave me a new gratitude for life. I appreciated the work of all the doctors and found new meaning in the adage: where there is health there is wealth. I spent a lot of my stay in hospital thinking about myself, and the fact that I would not have survived had I not received such great treatments.

In addition, don't forget how much strain events like this put on your immediate family. With both Caroline and me in different intensive care units and at opposite ends of the hospital, Marvin, my mum and sisters were constantly moving from one section of the hospital to the other to make sure that Caroline and I were receiving all the love and support we needed.

It's only later that you realise what an enormous strain, both physically and mentally, intensive caregiving puts on people, no matter how strong or how well prepared.

For Connor, upsetting his routine at the end of the school year was difficult for him, especially since he was waiting in anticipation to meet his new sister and it was tough for him to understand why he had to wait even longer to have her come home.

It is so important, when faced with such severe illness, that you try to remember to be grateful. The love, care and support I received was nothing short of miraculous, and at a time when I could have found myself sinking into depression, instead, I considered myself one of the luckiest women alive. To have been able to have two babies despite the overwhelming odds, and to have come through both those ordeals and have the opportunity to watch my children grow is a precious gift I will never take for granted, and for me, it has been the finest achievement of my life.

PART 2

IT'S ALL IN THE MIND

CHAPTER 19

THE MENTAL BATTLE

You might think that this is the end of the story and I lived happily ever after. But as any of you battling this cruel illness will know, there is never an end to the story, because it is a lifelong condition that does not get better. But even so, it seemed that by the age of thirty, all the things that had seemed so unreachable when I was a teenager were now mine: I had a Bachelor's degree, a Master's degree, a loving and caring husband, two children and a good job that I enjoyed. And yet...there were very many times that I was still so unhappy. I was still limited by my disease, still suffered regular bouts of extreme illness, and no matter how much I tried to focus on the positives in my life, I kept getting dragged back.

Sometimes it was a real struggle for me to understand why I was still so often dissatisfied. Why could I not feel grateful and happy for all the blessings in my life? I had so much, I had the world in my palm and I was still not as happy as I should be. Unfortunately, this is one of the most horrible effects of a chronic illness; it can plague your mind and subdue its strength.

The severity of the pain might fluctuate, but it's always there, humming in the background until the next time it comes crashing back to the forefront of my consciousness and turns my life upside down again.

One of the most difficult aspects of living with sickle cell is the sheer unpredictability of the attacks. From one hour to the next you can go from being happy and normal, to screaming in agony and being rushed to hospital. The reality for all of us with this cruel disease is that we always have to be prepared for things to change.

Living with this uncertainty is something we all have to get used to. Because for us, the phrase isn't '*Life* is what happens when you're busy making other plans.' It's '*Sickle cell*'. We need to be adaptable, accepting, and strong, because this disease throws curve balls at us from all directions and there are times when the obstacles we face can feel insurmountable.

A sickle cell crisis can feel terribly inhumane in more ways than one. The pain can actually drive you insane. And when you're not in pain, the *threat* of the pain can be just as – if not more – frightening.

The psychological impact of sickle cell can be incredibly damaging and is perhaps one of the most under-acknowledged consequences of the disease. Many people actually don't understand the impact of sickle cell on the mind, because it is associated only with physical pain. People often have trouble understanding the nuances of this disease; they can look at you and believe that you're completely fine when you're actually not.

Because however well we feel, however well life seems to be going, it's always there in the back of our mind that at any moment we could be rolling around on the floor screaming in agony. The sword of Damocles hangs over our head all the time, and the only way to deal with this if you want to live a fulfilling and joyful life is to do everything in your power to prevent another attack, while also trying to forget that you could get ill until you need to remember.

By this I mean, when you are well – or as close to well as you can be – you need to forget that this can change in an instant, because the pressure of living with that threat day-to-day, minute-to-minute, is too overwhelming. And, more to the point, it's *out of your control.* So set it aside, try to pretend it's not there, and keep putting one foot in front of the other, enjoying your life to the best of your ability. Control only what is within your power, and for the rest: PLAN! So that at least the anxiety of what will happen when you are next ill is taken away.

Unsurprisingly, given all of this, there is a close connection between sickle cell and anxiety and depression, and support systems need to be in place in order to prevent an inevitable emotional breakdown. While there have been times in my own life when I've felt unsure about my existence and/or future, I also realise that thoughts like these can be dangerous for both physical and mental health.

In my own case, there were times when the pain associated with sickle cell was so awful that I wished I could just be dead; I just couldn't take it anymore and wanted to give up. Thankfully, though, I have been blessed with a wonderful family who have been with me every step of the way, encouraging me and protecting my spirit. Their unwavering support and the unconditional love that they surrounded me with gave me the hope and the courage to go on, no matter what. They imparted mental fortitude to deal with this menacing illness and a strong determination to always try to conquer the pain.

It is this mental strength that has helped me survive the brutal onslaughts and made me a winner of sorts, because I have refused to succumb to this disease and have continued to pursue my dreams. My mental strength is challenged and frequently weakened by intimidating physical pain and mental agony, but never gives in and always defeats the seemingly undefeatable.

Accepting the reality of your life, understanding your issues and working to address this takes time and dedication, however. It took me many years before I understood my problem, especially because it wasn't just physical. I used to envy those with visible physical disabilities, as it seemed to me that no one questioned their need for help and support, whereas those of us with hidden disabilities are often deprived of the support we need because people are unaware we are struggling.

Sometimes this can take the form of having to justify our need for rest and days off work due to illness, because as far as others are concerned, we look fine. Sometimes this means even having to convince the doctor that the agony is as bad as it is. And, weirdly, when people question your experience, you start to question it yourself. You wonder, 'Maybe I am exaggerating. Maybe it's not so bad, and I should just keep going and stop making a fuss.' But of course, it's not possible, and it puts the sufferer in a horrible position, increasing their anxiety, which in turn increases their pain. It is a vicious cycle that many sickle cell sufferers have been caught in – I know that I certainly have – and it takes courage and mental fortitude to find your way out of it and achieve a better life for yourself.

And though, after Connor was born, I was proud of where I had come in life, I knew there was still so much that wasn't right with my own mindset. If I was still unhappy even though I had so much, then there was still work I needed to do on myself. I just wasn't sure what or where to start. What I was sure of, though, was that no medicine could help me. I already had the best medical care I could hope to have, so physically, there was no more that could be done for me. No, what I needed was *mental strength*, and that is something only I could give myself.

CHAPTER 20

CREATING A POSITIVE MINDSET

The mind is a funny thing. On the one hand, it's remarkable. But on the other, it can crush us more quickly and ruthlessly than anything else.

The tendency of the mind to want to *control* what we are going through or feeling is so strong that we often underestimate the effect of this in our lives. I have learned over the years that the problem isn't our mind, per se, but how we use it to control a situation. By choosing to try to control that which is not within our power, we set ourselves up for failure and disappointment – leading to an inevitable loss of self-esteem and belief in ourselves, and an increase not only in our mental pain, but also our physical pain.

Since my early teens, I have known that sickle cell has the ability to influence my mind in a profound manner by predisposing my emotions in a certain direction – usually negative! It goes without saying that our attitudes can make the agony far worse than it actually is, especially when it comes to chronic pain. Such is the power of our mind that it can amplify or lessen the intensity of physical agony.

In the past, my biggest worries have always stemmed from the negative thoughts that encroach on me when I think

I am about to have a sickle cell attack. At this point, I would often be beset with anxieties, such as: how long will I be in hospital? What if the doctors can't find a vein to administer the IV treatment? What will other people say about me being sick again?

In short, just when I needed to be at my strongest mentally, a range of emotions and worries would overwhelm me.

But if I have learned one thing, it is that the mind and the body are two sides of the same coin. When you think of something with a powerful intent and utmost concentration, you sometimes end up becoming what you have been thinking about. For example, when you begin to think of pain, your body can actually start to feel pain, because it is so used to feeling it. I would often think my body was in agony when it was not. Interestingly, when it wasn't in torture, I used to ask myself why am I not feeling hurt? Some mornings, I would wake up in a panic, dreading how the day would unfold in terms of what kind of pain I would experience, or if I would even experience any pain at all.

I have spent weeks in hospital being pumped with drugs and still not felt like I was getting better. I'd often ask myself, why should I be getting better at all? I have a lifelong illness that is not going to go away; I'm not supposed to get better and I should be used to this by now. And, without doubt, it was my state of mind at these times that was holding back my recovery.

Compounding my worries at those times was a widespread notion surrounding sickle cell that some sufferers become morphine addicts, leading to them going to hospital or to see their doctors whether they need the pain medication or not, just to feed their addiction.

Morphine is a powerful and effective painkiller used to treat our pains. It blocks pain and calms some of the functions of the central nervous system by slowing heart rate and respiration, lowering blood pressure, and enhancing a sense of calm and pleasure. It can lead to dependency if taken too frequently over a period of time and some medical staff confuse this for addiction. It isn't always easy to tell the difference, because a physical dependence on drugs often accompanies addiction. But in the case of those of us who take drugs to treat a chronic physical condition, a need for higher doses or more frequent prescriptions usually indicates either a growing tolerance for the drug or a worsening underlying problem, and *not* addiction.

As a consequence of this attitude there have been times when I have felt I needed to justify my need for painkillers to some doctors who didn't always realise just how much agony I was actually in. But, even so, the thought would be in my mind: did I really need the medication I had been taking to ease my ache? Or was it because I was an addict who could not do without it? It's little wonder, then, that with these negative and confused thoughts running round and round my mind that my recovery at times was slow.

In fact, in reality the drugs terrified me beyond measure because the strong side effects were often as bad as the hurt itself. They made me feel different to my normal self: fuzzy, short-tempered and sleepy. My mother would always urge me to go to the hospital for my pain treatment, but I found it to be a scary experience that dented my mental strength. Strange as it may sound, I would often feel more scared when I was feeling better than when I was experiencing a sickle cell crisis, just because of the overriding fear of it happening again. I would always worry about when the next attack would engulf my body, and these thoughts left me feeling extremely worried and unsure about most things in my life.

My mum would often say to me, 'You must train your

mind not to think these horrible thoughts.' I would normally reply, 'Mum, I can't. All I can think of is the side effects I normally have after a sickle cell attack.' She would answer back, 'You have to just do it or you have to go to hospital, because otherwise you will make yourself worse.'

I would get so confused with this on-going battle between my body and my mind that when I wasn't sick, I would be thinking about getting sick and it put me in a very negative headspace. I tried my best to get away from such compulsive and negative thoughts, but the harder I tried, the more trapped I felt. This was a debilitating feeling that I wanted to get rid of as soon as possible but was unable to, because I was allowing my pain to rule my life completely.

The aching I go through is deeply personal, unique and different. Hence, encapsulating my sufferings, experiences and emotions is a very difficult process because some things cannot be explained in mere words. But what I have learned is that it is essential to find ways to stop yourself worrying about your hurt, and start thinking about the long-term impact of emotions on your health. This is absolutely vital if we, as sufferers of chronic pain, want to live a happy and fulfilling life. Since aches can affect your emotions adversely, this, in turn, causes your body to react in an adverse manner because our mind and body share a symbiotic relationship and anything that effects one will consequently have an impact on the other.

One of the keys for me in learning to deal with my pain was understanding my personality. This has only been possible as I've matured and realised what makes me who I am. I can be driven, and I am competitive, and these two factors have made it difficult for me not only to accept my limitations, but also to accept that sometimes I have to live at a slower pace than I'd like.

This is something that's led to trouble for me in the past. For example, when I was younger, I made everything worse for myself because I was a typical older sibling who demanded perfection from myself. I always wanted to please my sisters and my parents in any way that I could. I wanted to do the right things the right way and be a good example for my sisters, so I tried to lead by example, pushing my own limits despite knowing very well that I was exhausted and there was only so much I could do.

Those times at school when I was in the same school year as my younger sisters were torture to me because I felt like a failure. I felt that, no matter how understanding and wonderful my sisters were, that it was *I* who should have been helping them with their lessons. I should have been able to give advice about life or school or boyfriends, but my circumstances meant I never could. I always felt I was lagging behind. As a result, during my teens, I was constantly ill because I just did not know how to manage the unrealistic expectations that I had set out for myself.

You can see from the chapters about my numerous exam failures just how badly sickle cell affected my life and my dreams, and how, if I had not had the wonderful support I had, I could have given up. And it's why I feel so strongly that children should be taught from as early an age as possible strategies for coping with their pain with their mind, not just with medicine.

People – and I suppose by that I mean those who don't suffer from sickle cell – often look for external causes for pain. But this is a flawed approach because it ignores the most common reasons for aggravating sickle cell pain, which include stress, anxiety and tension. These are all factors that can be triggered by a number of areas in our lives – ranging from family conflicts to stress at work, or difficulty in managing the expectations of ourselves and others.

It's important to realise, too, that learning to control how you react to your illness does not mean you have to change your personality. For myself, I haven't really changed. I am still a perfectionist with a mild obsessive-compulsive disorder, which is a serious anxiety-related condition where I can experience frequent intrusive and unwelcome obsessional thoughts about my pain. In short, I put pressure on myself and turn my thoughts about the pain into a self-fulfilling prophecy.

But gradually, with help, I have learned to deal with these demons and understand my responsibilities better – my responsibilities to myself and also to my family because they are affected just as badly by sickle cell as I am. Their lives are disrupted and their own fears and sadness surrounding my illness can overwhelm them just as much as mine can. So I have learned to accept that I cannot be all things to all people, but instead I must live the best way I can, without comparing myself to anyone else.

To do this I have had to train myself to have happy thoughts. If negative thoughts come into my mind – especially of the self-pitying kind – I make a conscious effort to think about all the positive aspects of my life. It's easier said than done, of course, and it's something I've had to put a lot of effort into because after suffering chronic pain on a daily basis for so many years, it did not come easily to me. However, as I continued to adopt that approach, things became easier and much more manageable both medically and in clearing up my thoughts.

HOW TO BRING POSITIVITY TO YOUR LIFE

Being mentally strong means making some difficult decisions. But the important thing is that you make those decisions for good reasons. Because to stay positive and well, you need to avoid the things that bring you down. So the following is a list of steps I took to try to bring myself into the right mindset.

- **Let go of your anger.** This might be easier said than done, of course, but there are triggers for anger and upset and you need to be honest about them. For myself, this meant:
  - No longer seeing people who made me angry or upset. There are always people in your life with whom you might have a spiky relationship. Unfortunately, for those of us who need to stay mentally strong, this can be a drain and cause stress, so it is best to avoid this type of friendship.
  - Accept that people make mistakes (you know *you* do, right?) and try to see the funny side.
  - When someone says something that might upset you, try not to take it personally. Chances are, they didn't mean it that way anyway, so take a more relaxed, easy-going attitude to things that really don't matter.
  - Do not harbour resentments. They are harmful at the best of times, but when you suffer with sickle cell, they can make you sick.
- **Don't resent other people's happiness or success.** Be happy for them, as they would be happy for you.
- **Do not compare yourself with anyone else.** Worry only about yourself, your own happiness and those around you.
- **Be grateful for the people who love and support you.** Without them, your life would be immeasurably poorer, so remember to let them know how much you appreciate them.

- **Create opportunities to celebrate life and what you have with those you love.** When you come together to celebrate, it will remind you of how much you have to be grateful for.

CHAPTER 21

CHANGING YOUR ATTITUDE

Of course, I didn't come to all these realisations by myself. And though my family have been ever-loving and supportive, for family members, too, having a loved one with a chronic illness traps them into a cycle of care and worry; you are all together in this cycle, and sometimes patterns need to be broken.

Changing my mindset and attitude towards my illness has been a gradual process; a slow accumulation of lessons learned from experience, from doctors and psychologists and, obviously, from growing maturity.

But I do want to mention two people who helped me look at my disease and my reaction to it differently. And I thank them profoundly for the insights they gave me.

The first was my doctor, the late Dr Norman Parker, who took the time to talk me through a very painful period of illness. I first met Dr Parker when I moved my hospital to Whittington Health, as it was closer to home. He was always very keen to help me manage my sickle cell through a holistic approach. As a member of the British Nutrition Society he also worked with me to improve my understanding of the importance of healthy eating, which I will discuss more in Part 3. When I started following his advice, I was often surprised by the benefits that this simple measure brought.

But on this particular occasion, I was working hard and keen to prove myself. I had been due to go on a business trip to see a potential new client and I'd had high hopes that this client would not only impress my boss, but also help me in my bid for promotion. But instead, not long before I was due to leave, I was struck down with pneumonia. I became so ill that I was in critical care for a week as I was unable to breathe on my own and required intensive treatment and close monitoring. It is always difficult for my family to see me in hospital, especially on this occasion as I was strapped to monitoring equipment as well as having IV lines and pumps, feeding tubes and catheters – thin tubes inserted into the bladder to drain urine – attached. I was, of course, also attached to a drip that was administering my painkilling drugs.

After a week, I was moved to a general ward to continue my recovery before eventually being discharged. Towards the end of my hospital stay, while I lay in bed recovering, I couldn't stop the negative thoughts going round and round in my head. 'Why me?' I kept thinking, full of self-pity. This illness was not only ruining my career, it was actually preventing me from living my life. Why should I be the one to suffer so badly, while others got to live pain-free and without these frequent disruptions to their lives?

At this time, I was almost better, but still suffering from weakness and stiffness, extreme tiredness, loss of appetite and weight loss, depression, and problems with my mental abilities. However, despite this, I had high expectations of being discharged shortly and was hopeful of getting back to work and rearranging my meeting. But when Dr Parker came for his ward visit, accompanied by several colleagues, it was made clear that I would not be going home for another week and even if I did go home, I would not be signed off to travel for a while.

I was so mad and so upset that suddenly everything became too much for me to bear and I broke down in front of my doctor and his colleagues. Dr Parker tried to comfort me but I was inconsolable and nothing he said helped. So he left me to calm down.

He returned later after giving my situation some thought and said, 'Anne, you seemed very down earlier and I want to tell you that if you train your mind to endorse negative thoughts, then you will feel them with a much stronger intensity. You need to allow yourself to think positively. Sometimes, if a patient is feeling low, negative thoughts can cause their condition to deteriorate. No one is telling you that you can't live your life, but right now, you are ill and need to find other things that will make you happy. Try and be grateful you got ill before you got on a flight.' He then suggested I reflect, listen to music and bring books and magazines to the hospital to keep my mind occupied.

Grateful? I thought, indignant and still upset. I felt like a failure. I felt like a useless let-down who had simply nothing going for me. I was done with everything and did not want to lead such a miserable life. But gradually his words sunk in, and I started to reflect on what he had said.

Now, looking back, I am convinced that the doctor was my guardian angel. He wasn't trying to patronise me or belittle my experiences, he was merely trying to protect and help me become more optimistic and grateful for all the good things in my life.

After that conversation, I tried to remain positive mentally, regardless of my physical situation and the inconvenience it caused. I tried to count my blessings rather than bemoan all the negative aspects of my life. And I found it helped me greatly when I was recovering from illness, especially when it came to having patience with myself and letting go of those worries that were holding me back – like, for example, worrying that if I didn't get back to work soon I would be letting people down, which of course only increased my anxiety.

His words also made me realise that I had often mistaken people's concern for me as an insult to who I was – as if they thought I needed special treatment because I wasn't capable of looking after myself – when they only had my best interests at heart. They did not mean to belittle my concerns, rather they wanted me to consider them in terms of my *priorities*. And my first priority was to get well. And their first priority was to help me achieve that. And for that I should always be profoundly thankful. So many people wished me well and wanted to help me, and yet all I could think was that I was a failure.

It wasn't that their care meant nothing to me, rather, it was a frustration at the fact that they needed to care for me at all. And I can't deny, I'm afraid, that I have been guilty of taking out my frustrations on those I love the most. But without them, how much more difficult would life be? Would I rather have this horrible disease and these wonderful people who care for me? Or live pain-free and not have them in my life? The answer is very simple, and it led me to do some serious thinking and come to some sobering truths about myself and the way I dealt with my disease. What I needed, I decided, was to accept that this was how my life was, and find the joy in it. And I had plenty to be thankful and joyful for.

But I wasn't there yet! I still found it hard to control my negative thoughts, and moaned about my situation. Then I had another encounter in hospital. This time the wisdom came from a very different perspective. It came from someone who really understood what it means to live with this disease, someone who fought the same battle as I did on a daily basis. And as such, she made an incredibly powerful impression on me.

On this occasion, I was again in hospital following a crisis and I made friends with the woman in the bed next to mine. To this day, I do not know her name, but I thank her from the bottom of my heart. In the ward, most people I come across are elderly. She stood out instantly because not only was she young, but she was outgoing, which was unusual as sickle cell patients are normally subdued. We began a lengthy conversation about our disease, speaking until our pain overcame us and we had to rest.

The following day, we began to talk again about the frustration of the situation we found ourselves in, and the afflictions brought on by sickle cell. She said that when she felt particularly overwhelmed by her illness, her mother would always tell her: 'It takes courage to grow up and become who you really are.' I did not quite understand how she thought this might relate to me and the pain I was currently experiencing; it was something that perturbed me. She could see this on my face, and as I started to turn away from her, she stopped me and explained what she was trying to say.

She explained that sickle cell is a disease that is all-consuming; the pain is consuming and when this is your mind's default setting, you cannot help but think about the numerous difficulties it causes you. She said, 'You are in a bubble sometimes with this disease, and you do not want to become trapped in this bubble, which is why we need to take the courage we have and grow up and look at things in a different light. I promise you, if you do this, it will help the painful feeling go away.'

I reflected upon this and with the passage of time it began to make more sense to me. She, like the doctor on that other occasion, was telling me I needed to be grateful. I should be grateful for the care I was receiving, and for the fact that, thanks to this care, I would get better, get out of hospital and be free to pick up my life again. In short, I needed to grow out of my disease mentally and tackle it head on, rather than let it grind me down and cause me to feel depressed. Her statement began to resonate strongly in my mind and I realised that she made a lot of sense. I needed to be more courageous in handling my situation and not let it affect my happiness.

There is no doubt that these two people had a profound impact on me, an impact that only grew the more I thought about their words. And I gradually began to take ownership of my disease and my pain. I started to understand what helped and what didn't and to stick with my plans. By having tried-and-tested routines in place, and by changing the way I thought about my life, gradually life started to get a little better for me.

Notice the word 'gradually' here. Please do not think this can happen overnight. I had a lot of work still to do on myself, and there were others waiting in the wings who would also help. And their effect on me would be life-changing.

CHAPTER 22

TAKING OWNERSHIP OF YOUR DISEASE

I would suggest to anyone suffering with sickle cell that there are some practical steps you can take to help you come to terms with your disease and hopefully reduce the number of crises that you suffer (see Part 3). But there are also some mental adjustments that you need to make. For me, I realised that the following steps were all necessary if I was to take some control of my life, try to release my fear and avoid falling down the rabbit hole of depression and anxiety:

- **Reduce stress and anxiety.** It would be wonderful to be able to live without stress, but as that's not possible for anyone you need to find ways to prevent the stress you *can* control. Whether it's avoiding unnecessary conflicts with those around you, to reducing the stress you feel around your disease. So now, if I start to feel emotions or anxiety overwhelming me, I physically stop whatever I am doing, and take stock of my surroundings and think honestly about what it is that's worrying me or making me angry. If it's fear of the next attack, then I reassure myself of all that I know: I am in a safe environment and I am feeling good, so I need to keep going and not think about what might happen. When I feel myself getting sick, I try to close my mind to all the trivial anxieties that used to assail me – How long will I be in hospital? What if the treatment doesn't work? What will others think? – because they are out of my control. Instead I try to think about the fact that my doctors know exactly how to treat me to get me better as quickly as possible. And I consider that in a week or two, I will be better, and life will continue as normal.

If it's anger at a situation or with a person, I will myself to let it go. I think about how, if in a day, two days, I won't even remember the cause of my anger, it is not important enough to worry about now. If it is a problem that needs solving, I sit and think calmly of solutions, instead of allowing myself to feel overwhelmed. Plus, I talk to those I love. Sharing the problems and your anger can put it all in perspective and bring you back to a sense of calm.

- **Acceptance.** Working towards acceptance has been a lifelong project for me. I am better at it today than I was as a teenager, but even so, there are times when I want to scream against my situation. I know this doesn't help me, I understand that it won't make the pain go away, but when you are in such desperate agony that all you want to do is disappear, it's difficult to control your mind. But this is the reality of your situation. Try to relax into it, don't fight. It's going to run its course, and the more anxious and overwrought you feel, the longer it's going to take to recover. But if you accept the inevitable and stop fighting against it in your mind, you will be able to look outwards and see that you can get through your current agony.

- **If you can't, you can't.** This seems obvious, but there have been times when I have ignored what my body was telling me and kept going. Or not gone to the doctor when I felt sick. There's no getting away from your disease, and denying that you feel ill will only make you sicker in the long run. Equally, allow yourself the time you need to recover. Don't rush back to work, for example. Or go food shopping when you've just got out of hospital. Rest, recuperate, and try not to stress about when you'll feel better because if you do, it could send you spiralling back down into a crisis. I've done this on many occasions, but I now understand that if I can't, I can't, and by accepting that, I have stopped putting pressure on myself to be superwoman.

- **Have your plans in place.** Sometimes attacks cannot be avoided, so you need to know that, if you are hit with a nasty episode, no matter where you are, you will be taken care of. One of the things that used to worry me greatly about having an attack was that I might not get the treatment I needed quickly enough. This was especially the case when I was out, or with people I didn't know well – which of course meant I was anxious, which in turn increased the likelihood of my having an attack. So you need your contingency plans in place. A number on speed dial, perhaps. Or, if you are at work, colleagues who know exactly what to do if you need to go to hospital. If you are out on your own, you can wear a wristband, so if you are struck with an attack, someone will find it and know what's happened, ensuring you get to the hospital quickly.

- **Know what works for you and don't be afraid to ask for it.** For me, during a bout of crisis, my primary focus is to control my pain as quickly and efficiently as possible through rapid initiation of IV opioids or pain medications. This is important because the pace at which the misery intensifies can be unpredictable and leave me feeling hopeless. The sooner I am able to control the pain to manageable degrees, the better it is for me. So when I am suffering with a sickle cell crisis, hospital admission is usually key to speeding up my recovery. This is because when I receive round-the-clock pain medication via IV or oral opioids, my agony scores are reduced, as compared to using pain management on an as-needed basis. In addition, IV hydration helps me avoid over-hydration, while also ensuring that there is enough fluid to dilute the sickle cells. Subsequently, frequent reassessment of my treatment plan is essential to ensure that my ache remains controlled for a substantial period of time. This allows me to manage my disease better and focus on other things. And if you know that your care is the best it can be, you will be able to relax and get on with your life.

- **Be grateful.** It's so easy when you are tired and dispirited to think, 'Why me?' Believe me, I have done this far too often for my own liking. And yet, there are always so many good things to take joy from in your life. Try to focus on these when you feel that dark wave of depression coming at you. And if you find that doesn't work, then perhaps try some distractions. Now when I'm in the hospital, I make sure I keep myself active and mobile. I go for a walk; I look at the trees and count the leaves. Doing small and unimportant things like this imparts a sense of accomplishment, as though I've done something worthwhile. It is better not to wallow in self-pity or hopelessness because that is not going to get you anywhere.

- **Be kind to yourself.** Sometimes you will slip up and find yourself falling into old habits and old thought patterns. Don't let this be the prelude to a downward spiral in your thoughts. Distract yourself as best you can and forgive yourself. It's not easy being positive when you're ill, but each time you find yourself back at square one – in pain and in hospital with your life on hold again – see if you can change your mindset in small ways. Just by taking an interest in what's happening around you, you can distract yourself from spiralling deeper into despair.

CHAPTER 23

MAKING PROGRESS BUT COULD DO BETTER

After having my son, I started to learn how to manage my pain more effectively and to reduce my anxiety to an extent. Plus, my life was busy with work, and everything that comes with being a working mother.

But what had not disappeared was the feeling that I was ruled by my disease and there were times when I still felt trapped in a cycle of illness and self-pity. If I had had a school report on my state of mind at the time it would probably have said: Making progress, but could do better!

Your mindset can really alter the way you are and how you feel about yourself. When you constantly scare yourself into thinking the worst, it often actually makes it come to pass. My mind had been programmed to be scared, to think about the fact that I could not do normal things, to fear everything for so long that it should not have surprised me that changing this attitude would take years – in fact it is always a work in progress. The problem was I still didn't entirely understand what that change of attitude looked like.

Certainly, I had overcome all manner of obstacles, and on occasion, by thinking positively and taking proper care of myself, I had managed to achieve my goals almost through sheer force of will – gaining my degree and organising my wedding were two particular achievements when I practically *willed* myself to be well. But even so, I still had not fully embraced this attitude. Rather, I seemed to keep it for special occasions, when what I needed was to think like this *at all times*.

For example, it was not just at the onset of a sickle cell attack that I could become overwhelmed. I also tended to associate certain activities and sports with pain. So, even now, I find myself creating 'pain patterns' that can bring on more agony through self-induced anxiety and stress. I absolutely hate this feeling because it makes me feel disempowered and disoriented; I know what I am doing is not right, but there are times when I have no control over my emotions and end up exacerbating my own misery.

When you suffer from a chronic condition, whether it is mental or physical, every day can start to feel like an uphill struggle. And sometimes there are days when you feel as if you are fighting a losing battle and there is no end in sight. The non-stop pain becomes an integral part of you, and affects the way you behave and express yourself to the world. It almost becomes an extension of you – second nature. And it can be exhausting – both physically and emotionally – to the point where you feel you are powerless to do anything more. All you can think of is minimising your pain and keeping yourself within the 'safe' boundaries that you have set for yourself. For example, there came a time when I stopped trying to walk too far because walking caused me pain and made me exhausted. And yet walking is something that most people take for granted and not having that was a constant source of distress to me.

Our lives are physically restricted in so many ways compared to healthy people's, yet even so, possibly the greatest restriction of all, is the one we impose on ourselves. *We imprison ourselves inside our fear and our anxiety*, and it is *this* more than anything else that we need to try to overcome.

What I knew, but didn't know how to change, was that I was still not living the life *I* wanted. There were still times when I would bemoan my condition. I still blamed everything that went wrong in my life on sickle cell. It was so much easier than taking that responsibility on myself. And, if I'm being entirely honest, and meaning no disrespect at all because their intentions were good, my family and my husband were complicit in this as well. We were *all* living in my sickle cell bubble, without even realising it.

Their attitude always came from a place of love and care, but I relied on them to make decisions for me, when really, as an adult, I could have made them for myself. This is a habit many people with chronic illness and their families have and it is never done consciously, nor is it malicious. It is the natural desire of the family to look after their sick loved one. And when you are sick, it is natural to let them.

I needed to find another way to lead the life *I* wanted as an adult, regardless of my disease, and this desire for self-determination is perhaps the most powerful tool we have. And it is one we must learn to use if we are to make the most of our lives, and find joy and fulfilment despite our disease.

CHAPTER 24

LIVE THE LIFE *YOU* WANT

Let me explain what I mean.

My mother has always been an incredible support to me. She is a wonderful woman and throughout my life she has been at my beck and call; she wants to be everything for me at all times. And I can understand that, especially now that I have two children of my own. As a parent, you don't want anything to harm your babies, or make them feel sad. If you could take their pain, you would. And I know this is how my mother felt. Especially as she was very well acquainted with the pain and grief of losing a child.

When we moved back to England, I found it very hard. Having failed to get into the same school as my sister and cousin, I already felt like a failure, and the constant struggles thereafter – the GCSE retakes, the A levels – made me so unhappy. And this, on top of the cold weather and the fact that by trying to fit in with my peers I was not taking care of myself as I should, I was constantly ill. I relied on my mother and my sisters completely for everything – for care, for comfort, for company. And they gave it all to me willingly. But my mother especially.

I was ill so often during that time that my mother's

overriding fear was that she would lose me, and so she did everything in her power to make sure that wouldn't happen. But by not allowing me to even lift a finger to help myself, she inadvertently disempowered me. And it was a co-dependent relationship. She needed to spend all her time ensuring I was safe and looked after as a way of reassuring herself that she was keeping me well. And I, in turn, was anxious not to do anything that would upset her, so I let her. And, to be honest, when you are struggling so much with pain and mental anguish, who doesn't want to be looked after? She controlled my life totally: what I ate, when I went out, who I went out with. For her, the overriding impulse was to keep me safe. And I didn't have the energy or the will to rebel against it. I wanted it, I felt I *needed* it.

However, there came a time when I realised that I was living my life through her and for her; I was living my life to make her happy, which was not a bad thing in itself, but there was more to life than just that. I would eat the food she wanted me to eat, make friends with the people she wanted me to be friends with. And while I know that she only wished the best for me, it stopped me from being able to explore my own life to the fullest and experience my own adventures.

For instance, I did not know or realise the indescribable joy that eating can give you. The different flavours and aromas from foreign cuisines can bring you so much pleasure. You also meet other people when you are dining; you can have conversations with people with whom you have a lot more in common than you realise. It sounds like a small thing, but I didn't realise for a long time that eating could be a social event. I had become so fearful of what I ate, as my mother was extremely particular about my diet, that I had missed out on such an important and exciting part of life: something that could make me feel blissful and forget about my pain for a time. I never stepped out to restaurants, fearing that they would not be able to offer me anything I could eat. My dedication towards making my mother happy had been getting the better of me. It had made me socially ignorant and when you cannot relate properly to others, it can have a very negative effect on your interaction with those around you. If you add this to the already intense feeling of sickness, you truly begin to feel like a social outcast.

Socially, I missed out on a lot when I was growing up. Even as an adult, I did not go to the halls of residence at university because my mother was too concerned that I might suddenly become unwell and not know how to deal with it. And maybe she was right, but it meant I missed out on that crucial social experience that gives so many young people their first true taste of independence. She was too worried about my well-being, which is something I cherish and treasure. However, I constantly felt as though I was missing out on some great opportunities, and this began to engulf my mind.

It felt as though my illness had stigmatised me for life, even within my family, in a subtle but strong way. It had prevented me from finding my own inner peace. I did not know who I was for a long period of time; I felt like a shadow of a person. It felt as though my main purpose in life was just to be unwell, go to the hospital, come out of it, get unwell again and go back in. When you're sick, everyone thinks they know what is best for you and for a long time, I had gone along with that because I was so used to it. But I did not know who I was, what I should be doing, or who I was supposed to be.

Everyone is so protective of you, in a nice way, and they are so scared that they might lose you that it can be suffocating at times. It was a real struggle for me to try to break away from that pattern, and it is when you're unwell that you become so dependant.

However, you must fight for what you feel is right for you if you want to be happy. You should be allowed to stand up and make your own choices and your own mistakes, because if you don't, you will never be satisfied with the life you lead and you have a right to live your life the way you want to.

When I started work, it should have been the start of a real push for independence for me. From the outside, it must have looked as though my life was starting to come together. And in one sense it was, but I was still some years away from understanding why, despite everything, I still wasn't completely happy, and was still dissatisfied.

At the time I was living at home, and though I had met Marvin, in many ways my mother and I were still living as we had since I was a teenager. Possibly, my first inklings of discontent came around this time as my mother would often try to stop me from going to work if she thought I was too unwell and that would upset me because although I could see how much she worried, she could not fully grasp how much I enjoyed my work environment. For me, work was a priceless joy. It was good for my mental health to be there, rather than to sit at home and wallow in front of the television, fearing that I might begin to feel unwell at any moment. I know she is my mother and wants only the best for me, like all other family members, however there are times when they are unable to understand the fact that being independent and in charge of my own destiny makes me feel truly happy and in control. In fact, even *I* didn't realise this. Or if I did, I hadn't given those thoughts proper consideration.

Having an illness is hard enough, but if you do not know who you are, or how you fit in to the world, then it will only add to that pain. I have spent almost my whole life constantly second-guessing myself, not trusting myself, believing that I cannot do certain things or that I will not be good enough at them, no matter how hard I try. I was floating through life for many years without any sense of purpose.

Even when I married – which you might think was a symbol of my growing independence – in many ways Marvin took over my mother's role. Although, of course, it was not quite the same, but when we were first together and in the first years of our marriage, I was sick quite a lot, and it was only natural for him to want to take care of me.

In particular after my pregnancy with Connor when I was so ill, he became very concerned about me when I accepted a new role that would require a lot of travel. I understood his concerns, but I needed to see if I could do it. Sadly, I found the travelling exhausting and terrifying. I was always worried I would be stuck somewhere where I could not get treatment, or even that I might have a crisis on a plane! Just the thought could make me feel sick with anxiety.

Marvin was keen that I take a step back, take it easy and do less. And I agreed. Because this is how I had lived throughout my life. I was sick, so there was a lot I couldn't do. I rarely questioned it. Because it's true, there are things I cannot do – I cannot run a marathon, I cannot go swimming, I cannot sit in the cold, nor can I sit in the heat. I cannot drink alcohol or stay up late… But all of these are physical, practical things. They do not define me. They are just sensible decisions I make for myself because I know I can get sick if I do them. But there are also things I *think* I cannot do, so I don't try them. And at that point in my life, I didn't even realise it. All I knew was that I was still dissatisfied. I still felt suffocated by my life and the restrictions my disease placed on me, and this made me angry with myself. I knew something else had to change, but what?

CHAPTER 25

THE DAY THAT CHANGED MY LIFE (MY A-HA MOMENT)

The absolute turning point of how I changed my attitude to living with sickle cell came when I was meant to go on my first planned business trip with the former President of Nigeria, His Excellency President Olusegun Obasanjo, who I was working with on international affairs as his executive assistant in August 2011. This was my first dedicated business role after I had had Connor and after volunteering for the Sickle Cell Society.

Five hours before boarding the plane I become very sick and was rushed to hospital. I was so upset and angry with myself, with my disease and with the fact that I had become an inconvenience to everyone. Stupidly, I had not told the President about my sickle cell disease. As I was so sick and unable to communicate with him, my family made a call to him to tell him that I was in the hospital and would be unable to join him on the trip. The fact that I had sickle cell came as a surprise to him because I had never talked to him about it previously.

Later, when I was recovering at home, I was feeling very low emotionally to such an extent that I wouldn't talk to anyone. In short, my self-pity was out of control and I couldn't bring myself to answer his calls when he was checking up on my well-being.

I felt as if I was climbing a ladder, but I could only ever get so far before sickle cell sent me slipping right back down to the start. My disease was holding me back, and now it seemed that I wouldn't even be able to travel anymore as no one would want to bear that risk.

A week later, I found the courage to send a message to President Obasanjo to inform him that I was very sorry, but I was unable to travel and would have to step back from my job. I did not get the response I expected, rather, instead of accepting my resignation, President Obasanjo was understanding, kind and empathetic, and his wisdom came to the fore.

All my life I have lived in fear of how everything made me sick to such an extent that I never enjoyed the moments when I was in good health. Sickle cell disease had taken over my mental health, tricking me into thinking that I was going to have a sickle cell attack whenever there was an important moment in my life. This thought process drove me to depression, anxiety, insecurity and anger.

When President Obasanjo replied to my text, little did I know that it would be my 'a-ha moment'. The words have had such a huge impact on me that I have framed the text and live by them every day.

Anne,
Life is what you make of it & not where u find yourself. If you find yourself where u think is inadequate or deficient, don't grumble or degenerate into self-pity. Nobody ever has life absolutely as he or she wants. But we all have beauty & ability with possibilities in our lives to ourselves, families, communities, & in the service of humanity & of God your Creator who wants u to fulfil the purpose of your creation.
Baba

When I read the text, I was utterly stunned. I wasn't sure he understood the full extent of my disease and how I believed it restricted my life. As I was recovering from a crisis at the time, I had little else to do but reflect. I read and reread the text, and suddenly it was as if a light turned on in my mind. And, just like that, I snapped out of it.

I remembered that with sickle cell I did have some *pain-less* days and on those days when I was *pain-less*, I wanted to live my best life. For me that meant that if I was well enough, I would travel, but if a crisis happened an hour before I was meant to do something, I would not feel disheartened if I had to cancel because it was sickle cell telling me that I had to rest, and I should accept this as my reality, safe in the knowledge that another opportunity would present itself and it wasn't the end of the world. That is the only way I can describe it. Suddenly I was filled with renewed energy and hope. Reading President Obasanjo's words made me realise that self-pity was not the way forward but rather I should look at myself and be grateful that I am alive and I should appreciate what I have, no matter how small.

From that day I came to terms with my disability and worked on adopting a positive attitude. I realised that the disadvantages in our life are there to strengthen our conviction. They are not there to run us over. If you have the right mindset you will be able to overcome any challenges you encounter. As the old saying goes, 'Your attitude determines your altitude'.

I've had some wonderful advice and useful tips from many people over the years. But on that day, for some reason, President Obasanjo caught me at just the right moment and said just the right words. I needed to hear them, and I needed to understand them. And I needed to *act* on them.

I thought about what I'd managed to achieve so far, despite my negative mindset and frequent sickle cell attacks.

I thought about how, despite my terrible performance in school exams and the struggles I'd had growing up, I'd *still* managed to go to university and get a degree and then a Master's. I thought about how I should be proud of these achievements, and rather than assuming I *couldn't* do something, I should just assume I *could*, until proved otherwise. I needed to change my internal monologue from 'I can't, I can't, I can't' to 'I can, I can, I can!'

I began to see, finally, how maybe I was the one putting the restrictions on myself. I was always blaming my sickle cell when things went wrong or I felt unhappy. But it wasn't that. It was me! It was what was in my mind that was holding me back. I needed to *properly* take ownership of my disease, of my life, of my relationships, if I wanted to grow. And I needed to take some risks. I needed to take my life in my hands with God's guidance and other people's support, but the agenda of my life must not be left to sickle cell or to anybody for that matter, except to me and my God.

If I wanted my illness and pain to be managed in a proper manner, then my mind had to be strong enough to handle my situation as well as I could. More importantly, I wanted to steer the ship of my life myself without depending on anyone else. I had been depending on my family and Marvin for far too long and I knew this had to change.

That's not to say that this attitude didn't come with its own problems, and I still had to listen to my body and make sure that I was not taking on too much. I could not escape the fact that sickle cell is a severe medical condition and mental toughness alone will not make you better; this is a genetic condition and can never go away. This is more about centring yourself and realising that it is your body and you must take responsibility for taking care of it the best you can.

CHAPTER 26

CHANGE CAN BE SCARY

Moving on to a new role with President Obasanjo was scary, as the role required a lot of travel. But making the decision to enjoy my pain-less days helped me to manage my anxiety much better. The institutional problem of not being able to get travel insurance always played heavily on my mind. As I have already mentioned, most major companies will not even talk to me and the only insurance I can get does not cover me for anything related to my sickle cell. This means if I get sick from sickle cell I will not be covered. As you can imagine, getting sick while abroad causes major problems for me!

One occasion that springs to mind is when I was on a conference trip to Istanbul. I could tell I was starting to become sick, but I tried to soldier through until it became too much for me. I know, I know, I should have listened to my body! Bearing in mind that I didn't have any insurance cover, I knew that I would have to somehow get back to London to get treatment. How I would manage that, I had no idea, and I can't deny the anxiety this caused made my crisis even worse.

Luckily, I was at the conference with President Obasanjo, who was so very understanding and knew what needed to be done. He also understood the seriousness of my illness and the situation I was in, so he wouldn't consider abandoning me. The President and his aides managed to get me onto the plane and took me to Paris where they arranged for Marvin to come and rescue me. I really wanted to get back to my own hospital where I had a protocol in place and would get the right treatment straightaway.

Poor Marvin! He made an emergency dash to Paris as quickly as he could and virtually carried me onto the train back to London, where he took me straight to hospital.

Following this incident President Obasanjo's aide was so worried that he advised the President to disengage this dangerously sickly lady from his employment. The aide reminded him that I had been sick a month ago when I was in Nigeria on a trip to see him and had to be hospitalised for a week in Abeokuta. This was so serious everyone thought I was going to pass away. However, luckily for me, the President decided to stick with me. He was impressed with Marvin's quick action in getting to Paris and evacuating me back to London. This made him realise that if Marvin could take on this risk of managing me and my disease, why couldn't he?

But even so, travelling without insurance is a big risk for my family and me, but I am determined not to stop my life because I can't get insurance. I will just pray and hope I don't die, and maybe one day there might be someone willing to insure someone like me.

Unsurprisingly, this episode made Marvin concerned every time I went away. And I was concerned too. In fact, I was terrified. My worries centred mostly on becoming sick and being stuck in a place where they didn't know how to treat me.

In addition, flying was often difficult for me to cope with, so I would sit on the plane, worried that I might get sick, and by the time I arrived I would be a nervous wreck. But I persevered, and I started to realise that it was true. I could do more than I believed. If I listened to my body, took my medication, looked after myself to the very best of my ability, then there was no reason why I couldn't do more.

TRAINING YOUR LOVED ONES

I can tell you now, though, that just because this is what I decided I must do, didn't meant that I wasn't still tentative. It's not easy, when you're used to living in a self-imposed cage to decide to live a little more openly.

And then there was my lovely family. They needed to be told too. They needed to understand that rather than telling me that I shouldn't do something in case I got sick, they should trust me to make these decisions for myself. I was over thirty years old, I had a child, a husband, a job...surely, it was about time I grew up and stopped living like an invalid. So I told them that it wasn't up to them to look after me when I was well. I could do that for myself. I just needed to know that they were there to help me when I was sick.

I am sure this is a common situation for many people in my position: it's so easy to give up and let everyone else look after you and tell you how to behave. It's so easy to feel powerless when you have a chronic illness. It's a habit that we make in childhood when we need to be mollycoddled and ordered to rest. And it's a habit that you need to find a way to break.

Naturally, you still need to be mindful of your disease and the limitations on the way you live your life – this is common sense. But this is *your* disease, and it is *your* life. You need to be trusted to live it in the way you see fit and the way that makes you happy if you are truly going to understand who you are and what your place is in the world.

So, sit down with your loved ones and explain it to them. Ask them to please respect your decisions, even if they don't agree. There will be conflict, and sometimes it might be hurtful, but they will learn. They will learn that you need to fulfil your potential and work towards your own happiness, and though you are glad of their support, and advice – when asked! – their role is no longer to make those decisions for you.

Even my sisters needed to be reminded every so often when they urged me to take it easy, or suggested I needed to stay in, when I wanted to go out... Every time one of them said, 'Anne, are you sure...?' or 'Don't you think it might be better if...', all those many, many small instances of well-meaning advice that I used to rely on had to change. Now they had to understand that I no longer needed it. Because, no matter if they thought I couldn't or shouldn't, *I* was the one, ultimately, who was the best judge of that.

CHAPTER 27

MY DISABILITY BADGE AND ME

My final act in trying to change my mindset is one that not everyone can undertake. It was quite a radical act, and though I was scared, I went ahead anyway. I mentioned earlier that for many years I have found walking for any distance very difficult. Too much walking could bring on a sickle cell episode, and so I tried to avoid it.

You will remember that at university I had a disability coordinator – something that I valued greatly, and something I would urge anybody who is offered the same to accept, because without doubt I could not have managed without her.

And later, I did an internship at a bank on a disability scheme. Again, for me this was invaluable, and it gave me the introduction I needed to start my career. Without it, I may not have been able to find work as quickly as I did.

However, I had always been uncomfortable with the label. Being sick is one thing, but being classified as disabled is quite another. People with sickle cell are classified as disabled because of the life-limiting effects of the illness: physically, we may not be able to carry out the same tasks as more able-bodied people. For example, many of us find walking for long periods difficult, we cannot lift or carry heavy objects, we are unable to function in extreme temperatures, which might mean we can be house-bound during very cold or very hot weather... the list goes on, and there is little doubt that everyday life is much harder for those with a chronic condition or a physical disability than it is for everyone else.

However, I did not like to think of myself as truly disabled, and yet it seems the world saw it differently. Certainly when I was sick, I was most definitely physically disabled. But still, it weighed on my mind.

I was given my disabled badge – known as a Blue Badge – when I was at college so that I could drive to college and park close to the school, and though this was an absolute boon and made my life so much easier during those difficult days, now I was taking ownership of my disease and I was older and more confident, I started to wonder whether I relied on it too much. And I also wondered whether the negativity that often came my way because of it was affecting my mindset.

There have been many times over the years when I have been abused for parking in a disabled spot. I once came back to my car and found a note saying, 'Bitch! I saw you walking you are NOT disabled!' These incidents always made me so upset and made me feel disempowered. I would find myself sitting in my car and waiting for the street to be empty before I crept out, looking around me, feeling ashamed. And if I saw somebody, I would limp to justify the fact that I had a badge. So basically, I was making myself worse just to justify my existence. And inevitably, because in my mind I thought I should make myself look sicker and was anxious about other people judging me, I would become even more sickly. The power of the mind again! Just the thought of going out started to feel like a chore and my fear of judgement was imprisoning me.

These thoughts went around and around in my mind for a very long time. And every time I had another difficult encounter with someone who did not believe there was anything wrong with me, the worse I felt. This had not been a problem before I had my badge, when I was not classified as 'disabled'. At those times, when I was sick I wasn't able to go out, but when I was well, I would go out and live my life as normal. And this is what I needed to get back to. I needed to take back the power to be well – which sounds so strange, but this is how I felt.

After a very long time – bear in mind, I'd had my badge for more than fifteen years – I wondered whether, if I sent the badge back, would I *feel* less disabled. Well, there was only one way to find out and I took the decision to send it back. I never thought this action would be so liberating. Please remember this was a personal choice and I am not advocating this action for everyone with a chronic illness; you must always make use of every tool that can improve your quality of life, but for me, this was absolutely the right thing to do.

The moment I had done this, I was terrified. How would I manage? What would happen if I couldn't find a parking space? How would I walk further? And yes, there have been many moments that I've regretted the loss of it. Finding parking is often a nightmare, and even though I can walk a little further now, I still struggle to walk too far, so this has been the biggest disadvantage. But the advantages to my state of mind have been incalculable. It's almost as if that now I do not have acknowledgement of the fact that my illness carries with it the label of disability, then it must follow that I am not! It was the most powerful message I could send myself, and though it's been tough, it reinforced my new attitude to myself, my illness and my life.

In addition, practically speaking, it meant that I had to make a huge effort to improve my strength and my health. I needed to exercise regularly, eat only the healthiest of foods, and do *everything*, and I mean *everything*, my doctors told me. There are no short cuts to being healthy when you have a chronic disease. One sleepless night, one cold, one fall can lead to weeks of illness and recovery, so I had to take total control of my physical and mental well-being on every level.

THE LANGUAGE OF DISABILITY

I was very happy to learn that the Blue Badge scheme has been extended so that people with 'invisible' health problems can more easily apply for one. These changes will make a massive difference to so many people who are struggling. In a move being applauded as an 'important step in the right direction', people with disabilities including autism and mental health conditions will be able to apply for a Blue Badge. I really hope that this new policy will make individuals stop and think before judging somebody who has a disabled badge and yet is not visibly disabled.

However, personally, I would like it to go further. Services for the disabled are essential and often life-enhancing, but then, as I found with the Blue Badge scheme for disabled people, the label and the connotations attached to it can also sap your mental strength and self-respect. How much better, then, if people could be acknowledged and respected for the challenges they face and overcome every day, rather than made to feel inferior for all the things they cannot do and the extra support they need. I think that would be a huge step in changing the mindset of many, many people and setting them on a road of hope and achievement.

To achieve this, perhaps we need to change the label that people with health challenges – both mental and physical – live with. Like I said, being labelled 'disabled' has always bothered me. But would I have felt the same way if the scheme that was recently launched in Dubai had been pioneered here? I think it perfectly encapsulates what I have been trying to say about how labels can have an impact, not just on the individual, but in the wider world as well.

In 2018 His Excellency Sheikh Mohammed bin Rashid Al Maktoum, Vice President and Prime Minister of the UAE and ruler of Dubai, launched a National Strategy for Empowering People with Disabilities. This strategy is built on six pillars of support: health and rehabilitation; education; vocational rehabilitation and employment; mobility, social protection and family empowerment and public life; and social and sport. But to my mind, what makes his strategy truly ground-breaking, is that he also announced a change to the *language* around disability from negative to positive, from 'people with disabilities' to 'people of determination'.

He explained that, 'Disability is in fact the inability to make progress and achievements. The achievements that people of determination have made in various spheres over the past years are proof that determination and strong will can do the impossible and encourage people to counter challenges and difficult circumstances while firmly achieving their goals.'

Many people might be sceptical about this, or even scoff about 'political correctness', but words have power, not only in how you see yourself, but also in how other people see you. The word 'disabled' by its very definition is negative. And, inevitably, it sinks into your psyche, it colours the way other people perceive you, and it pervades your entire life. But to have your difficulties recognised and your achievements acknowledged as being hard-won and deserving of respect, now *that* is something we should aspire to instil into every single person who lives with physical or mental challenges. *That* is what I would like the world to acknowledge. And a simple change of language seems like a very good place to start.

CHAPTER 28

CHOOSE HAPPINESS AND JOY

I have spoken before about the comfort I find in my faith, but I have not spoken in depth, because I understand that many who do not share my beliefs may feel uncomfortable about it, or they might view it with scepticism. However, my faith has been so integral to my mental well-being that I do not want to gloss over it entirely.

To my mind, happiness can be described as a state of body and mind with external inducement, which gives you satisfaction with yourself. Attitude is a major contributory factor and, therefore, to a large extent, the choice is yours.

But when spirituality goes hand-in-hand with attitude, joy exudes from inside and it is almost inexplicable. Joy is superior to happiness and is more a matter of soul – it is spiritually induced. While you may be in the midst of an unhappy situation, you can still have joy inside you. Both are influenced by attitude – happiness with body and mind, therefore largely temporal, and joy with mind and spirit, therefore largely spiritual. In pain, you can be unhappy but still have joy. For instance, you can be in prison and feel unhappy and yet have joy inside you. Therefore, choose to be happy but more importantly bring joy into your life. I find this through prayer and meditation. What you cannot change, you can manage – make it light in your mind and consign it to God. It isn't easy to achieve. Joy requires a substantial amount of understanding, faith and trust: understanding of what is; reasonable faith in yourself, others and God; and total trust in God for His benevolence and total goodness. Your happiness is essentially in your hands while your joy is essentially in God's hands but you need to cultivate it.

I know my body and I understand my illness, and by trying to cultivate joy, my faith in my ability to live the life I want has grown steadily. I have confidence and large amounts of faith in my parents, my sisters, my friends, some of my teachers, my doctors and my husband who understands my situation and not only accepts me as I am, but stands by me and supports me. Working with President Obasanjo and having him receive me as a daughter in spite of my situation increased my confidence and faith in myself and enhanced my 'can do' spirit. But most importantly, I have faith and total trust and reliance in God Almighty, my Creator, the ultimate Giver of all that I have had and that I have enjoyed in life. There is nothing more important for your own mental health than choosing happiness and joy, no matter what you may possess or lack in life. You must endeavour to be happy and have joy in your heart.

The way in which you find that joy is entirely personal, but when you find the path that suits you, embrace it and commit to it, and it will hopefully bring you the peace you crave.

After all these years of struggling to come to terms with my disease and find a positive reality, I feel I have finally come to a place where I can say I am truly happy. It hasn't been easy, and it still isn't. Sometimes I have to remind myself of how far I've come from the dark days of my teenage years and remember that though life isn't always easy I am blessed in so many ways.

It was a process that I went through over time. But the most important factor was that I needed to keep myself as pain-less as possible to prevent hospital admissions and allow me to live my life with as few interruptions as possible. All of this means living within your physical limitations – but mentally? The sky's the limit.

By finding happiness and contentment in my own space, by knowing how I can damage myself through my own decisions, and by letting go of that anxiety, I feel that I have finally learned how to get the best out of my life. We always need to ask ourselves what our purpose is. It took me a while to recognise, but for me it lies in being happy and contented in my own space. By this I mean doing things that make me happy and finding peace. In the past, if I were asked to define happiness, I just wouldn't have known what the answer was – unless it was living without sickle cell, which is ridiculous and unachievable, so I should never have wasted my energy on the thought.

However, I did know what I wanted: a loving relationship, a family of my own, and independence. I just never thought I could achieve them because of my illness. Particularly when I was a teenager, I was sure that no one could love me, that I was too stupid to get a good job, that I would depend on my family for the rest of my life. These thoughts are depressing. Even writing them makes me depressed.

Now, though, I think I have come to the conclusion that happiness is the peace of mind we gain when we let go of all the troubles that are out of our control; happiness is finding peace no matter your circumstances.

I have lived with sickle cell all my life and I have accepted that to move forward I have to make the best of it by creating an environment in which I can live the best life I can. This is tough, but if you keep your mentality right, put your health first you will be able to achieve this.

When I was growing up, a lot of things made me happy but at the same time my circumstances often took away this happiness. For example, I was always happy when I was involved in events or doing things with my friends. But I would always become upset when I couldn't join in. This made it much more difficult to fit in as I was often anxious and upset about my situation. But looking back now, I have come to understand that everything happens for a reason and my life would have been more unhappy if I had taken part and become ill in front of my friends as a consequence – as happened on occasion.

It's hard to choose to be happy and find peace, particularly when you suffer with a chronic illness. Constant illness can cause depression and anxiety due to the frustration of not being able to fulfil your own expectations, the threat of unemployment – so common among sufferers due to needing to take so much time off work – and just not being able to live life in the same way as those who are well. All of this can take a toll on your mental health.

I have always been encouraged to have a positive outlook on life, but you can see from my story that I haven't found that easy to achieve. It's easy enough for someone to tell you to 'look on the bright side' but there were times when it seemed there *was* no bright side. Living with a chronic illness and having to battle constantly to find peace of mind is hard. We are so often dogged by misfortune, brought on by our ill health, and when you are just trying to get through each day, it is hard to find joy.

One of the keys to overcoming all of this is to create a calm and peaceful environment where you are comfortable and feel safe.

I would recommend taking these steps to help you achieve the peace and happiness they crave:

- **Remove negatives from your life.** It is easy today to look at other people's lives and find yourself feeling resentful and envious. Living in the social media age means so much is open for us to look at, and, of course, people only show the very best of their lives – or they lie! As much as the social media platforms can be useful to discuss the issues you are facing on a daily basis, it can also be harmful. There has been a lot of media attention on the bullying and intimidation that can occur online, and this is an ever-present danger, particularly if you like to express yourself honestly. In addition, social media posts can set unrealistic expectations and create feelings of loneliness, isolation, insufficiency and low self-esteem, all of which lead to anxiety, depression.

  To deal with these issues it is important first not to believe everything you see and to remind yourself that you are always doing your best. Try to look at social media like you would a movie and remember that most posts are edited to tell a story that will sell to an audience. Many people create an illusion, so from the outside it can seem like everyone else is happy, successful and fulfilled, when in reality, the truth is always different. Remember, everyone is battling with their own problems, they just choose not to show that to the rest of the world.

  I watched a video on YouTube recently to see how much editing goes in to some of the videos posted on the social media site. I was stunned at how easy it was to make a simple image of somebody look like they are walking on the red carpet. There is no disclaimer which states that you have to say if the pictures have been retouched so it is very difficult to know what is real and what is not.

To overcome this challenge, try to change your mindset from wishing to be like your friends by surrounding yourself with positive people who love and accept you just as you are. This way, the image of yourself that is reflected back at you is always a positive one – well mostly! And when you are at a low ebb due to illness, these people will support you and remind you that they love you, no matter what. And sometimes it might be necessary to take a break from social media altogether, and instead take pleasure in your own world, rather than comparing it to everyone else's.

- **Face Your Reality.** How do you know you are avoiding your own reality? Have you caught yourself constantly pretending that everything is OK when deep inside you know the truth? Like me when I was in pain but kept going, hoping it would go away on its own. Do you find yourself doing things just to fit in, when really you know you are suffering and need to take a step back to recover your strength?

  Pretending that everything is OK can be a defence against facing reality. But it is only possible to be truly happy and positive when our life reflects our real internal reality; and this can only come from an acceptance of yourself and your circumstances. If you find yourself feeling more frustrated, moody, irritable, angry, resentful, tired, disconnected, not efficient...despite your efforts to be happy and positive, it may be a sign you are fighting against yourself.

This was true in my case, as I always wanted to fit in no matter how inconvenient or difficult the situation might be. But it seemed that however hard I tried, eventually I found myself tripping over my reality, and feeling trapped.

But *the day I decided to let go of my unhealthy defence – to face and accept my life as it was – things started to work for the better.* I realised that it was all right not to be able to do everything other people could do; it was all right not to be part of a group, if their activities were impossible for me to keep up with. It was more important to concentrate on my own abilities and life, and not worry about how everyone else was living.

Being left out of a group gave me the opportunity to reflect on my life and face my reality; to go from *forcing happiness* as a way of trying to deny my illness and the way I needed to live, to *real happiness* as I learned to live life to the fullest, while also accepting the reality of my condition. As I got older, and my life started to reflect more of who I was, I found I didn't have to work so hard to be happy since real joy and contentment come from within.

But all of this did not come naturally or immediately. I had to teach myself various methods of Facing Reality. Try to create more pain-free experiences in your life and not overwhelm yourself with more hospital admissions.

Ask yourself the following questions:

1 Is the source of your unhappiness something that you cannot change? For example, your illness. If that is the problem, try to learn to accept your circumstances and control the problem,

rather than fighting against the impossible and allowing it to control you.

2 Is there anything that you can change but you choose to let it be? That is OK, as long as you actively make the choice to let it be and know why you make that choice and how it impacts your life. One of those things for me was my disability badge.

3 And finally, what is it that you really want to put your energy into actively changing – the change that you can make and that can start shifting your life into a new direction?

In summary, the key to happiness is never straightforward. But though we are controlled by our circumstances to some extent, it is how we use our mind that can have the greatest effect on how we live our lives. So remember the following:

- Remove negativity from your thoughts by reducing and avoiding unnecessary conflict as this will not only drain you emotionally, but it has the potential to make you very ill.
- Do not put unrealistic expectations on yourself. Understand yourself and your limitations and create your life around those. If work is disrupted or you're unable to go on a planned holiday due to illness – whatever it is, try not to fret about it. Nothing is so important that it cannot wait for you to get better and new opportunities will replace the ones you had to miss. Staying healthy is the key to being happy.
- Accept you can't do everything you'd like to. Don't be upset if you can't do an activity or go to a social event because you are too tired, or physically you couldn't cope. Instead, create a world around yourself

that is full of possibilities for you, and, this is key, *allow others in*. The people you love will want you to be happy and will fit in with you.

- Be your best friend and try to prioritise activities that will make *you* happy or improve *your* life in some way. Obviously, life can get in the way, but, for example, by making sure you eat well, do exercise, regularly see people you love, and engage in work that interests you and keeps you motivated, then you can keep a positive outlook, even when ill.

It sounds easy, but of course it isn't. Everyone's life is a work in progress, but if you look after yourself first, you will have so much more to give those around you. So be kind to yourself. Always.

PART 3

LOOKING AFTER YOUR BODY

CHAPTER 29

TREAT YOURSELF WITH LOVE AND CARE

Giving up my disability badge brought me to another realisation. It's something that I had known all along, and it is part of the mental battle, but when confronted with the reality of *trying to prove that I was well as opposed to trying to prove that I was disabled*, I realised that there was another mental battle to fight.

We all know that disempowering thoughts can lead to stress and stress can lead to sickness. As a person who suffers from a chronic illness, *you must take care of yourself as the most important person on this planet* – because you are. If you're unwell, not only will you suffer, but you will also cause a lot of misery to your near and dear ones. *It is your prime duty to treat yourself with respect, dignity and care.* You must be in charge of your mind if you want to control your pain and not let it paralyse your life completely.

Pain can consume your body and your general well-being, but I have found that getting into a more positive headspace is the best remedy to handle it, or to at least make it more bearable. If you are unwell, you must surround yourself with positive people and stay in a positive environment or it can be a long, treacherous road for you. I have lived my life both ways – on the one hand trying to live for others and make others happy while neglecting my own well-being, and on the other making a conscious effort to lead my life the way I want to. And I can promise you that the latter is the one that has truly brought me the happiness I craved.

For me, it has been the only way to prevent my illness from taking over and tainting all aspects of my life. If I had succumbed to the pressure of my intense pain without giving my mind a chance to fight back, I would have been in a much worse state than I am right now.

But, as you might have noticed, none of this has come easily! It's been a lifetime of lessons and revelations. The mind consists of many different parts that can each influence the way you behave. *You* are the only one who can change how influential each part of your mind is.

And one aspect of your mind that you absolutely need to get to grips with is *self-control*. Everyone knows that lifestyle affects your health. But for those of us with chronic illness it is even more true. There can be few deviations from the path of being careful if you want to avoid getting sick. And it's not easy, day after day, to make sure you look after yourself. Sometimes you just want to stay up late, or you want to have that extra drink. But the consequences can be extreme and painful. So developing self-discipline is a major step on the road to living as healthy a life as possible. You need to learn to apply self-control over the behaviours you want to change.

To try to stay as well as possible, I needed to look after my body to the very best of my ability, and this meant improving my lifestyle – I needed to rest, drink plenty of water and eat foods that give my body all possible nutrients to fight off illness and reduce the possibility of having more crises. And, more than that, I needed to do the one thing I had avoided doing all my life – exercise!

And, you know, those doctors are right: good, nourishing food and regular exercise really do improve your health!

CHAPTER 30

EATING FOR A HEALTHIER YOU

I have talked about the hard part of taking control of my life – my mental battle to overcome my fears and to truly break free of the shackles sickle cell had put on me.

Now, on to the easier bits. Well, I say easier, but they can be tedious and sometimes sticking to a strict health regimen can be difficult when life is hectic and illness brings you down. However, the everyday physical care that you need to do to keep your body healthy and try to stave off painful crises is a key part of enabling you to live the best life you can. Diet and exercise are essential for everyone if they want to stay healthy, both mentally and physically. But for those of us with sickle cell, they are absolutely crucial. Because if you can keep your body as healthy as possible, it will help your mental attitude. It will also enable you to recover quicker should you become ill. The healthier you feel, the more you can do, and the closer you can come to living the life you've always craved.

It seems strange now, but the connection between diet and health was not something I ever understood when I was younger. Nor did my family. At that time, nutrition and the benefits of eating healthily was not taught at school, nor was it quite so widely publicised, so it never occurred to any of us to look at my diet and wonder if it was having an effect on my health. Rather, we associated diet with losing weight, and as people with sickle cell are always thin, my family were keen to avoid that at all costs. We never once considered that what I needed was a healthy diet that would help me maintain or even put on weight, and also provide all the nutrients my body needed.

In addition, I have always been very fussy with food, and so when I was a child, my parents tended to just give me the food I loved, because it was easier, and at least I was eating *something*. And of course, because I was a child, the food I loved tended to be very unhealthy.

It wasn't until I was seventeen that diet first came to my attention. This was in Nigeria, and I had been very sick and nothing seemed to be helping me get better. I was in hospital for three weeks and when I was discharged, within six hours I was admitted again. Everyone was losing hope, and no one could understand why I wasn't recovering. Then my aunty did a bit of research and suggested I see a nutritionist as she thought that the toxins in my blood could be eradicated by eating certain foods. The doctor saw me in hospital and seeing my green complexion, he immediately knew what was wrong. He put me on a two-week leaf diet, which was a liquid diet with a mixture of African medicinal plants and vegetables.

Let me tell you, this was the most disgusting thing I had ever tasted and I found it really difficult to follow his instructions. But because I was in so much pain and had no appetite at all, I went along with it. Within three days the pain in my legs slowly went away and my chest X-ray also improved. In addition, my blood results had improved. Delighted, my family ensured I continued drinking this juice, and without a doubt it helped me get back on my feet.

At last, the penny had started to drop that food had

an effect on my health. So I started making small changes to my diet, and I continued to drink my disgusting drink at least once a day. My family also helped clean up my diet by making sure I ate all the healthy foods I enjoyed like fruits and vegetables, rather than the junk I had been eating from the stores. I started to put on a few pounds, which made me look much healthier and my skin became much better. All in all, the effect was quite miraculous.

Unfortunately, when we moved back to England when I was eighteen, the health drink was no longer available to me. I also lost the habit of eating healthily. At the time, my mother was very busy looking after us and holding down a full-time job so she would normally prepare our meals for the week over the weekend, but as she wasn't there when we got home, my sisters and I would skip the meals she'd prepared and just eat junk food. And, of course, I started to get very sick again.

But not only was I sick with the usual complaints, I also discovered I had gallstones. Sickle cell sufferers are known to have problems of the digestive tract – thirty to fifty per cent of us will suffer from gallstones at some point – and I am no exception. The pain of the gallstones taught me that I needed to steer clear of fatty foods and fizzy drinks, but unfortunately, this was all I craved after I'd been sick.

To make matters worse, the high levels of morphine I was being given to treat my many painful crises was having a long-term effect on me. When I was in Nigeria, I took far less painkilling drugs than I did when I was in the UK. This is because drugs are so expensive in Nigeria that I tended to only go to hospital when the pain got too much to bear. Even then, I would be given only the minimum to get me through because the cost was so high. But in the UK, we are so lucky to have the NHS, and whenever I had a crisis, morphine was administered as a matter of course. But while this controlled my pain much more quickly, and consequently speeded up my recovery, my body just wasn't used to it, and the side effects were brutal. Aside from the irrational mood swings, fuzzy-headedness and itchiness I have already mentioned, it also gave me terrible constipation.

As a consequence of all the morphine I have taken over the years, my bowel movements have become almost non-existent, and this may be a something many of my fellow sufferers recognise. It is yet another reason to be careful with your diet. When I first noticed that I was getting a lot of constipation, I asked the doctors about it. They told me that I had developed Irritable Bowel Syndrome (IBS) and I should eat better and drink more fluids, but this didn't work as the drugs also meant that my appetite suffered, and the only things I wanted to eat and drink were fatty food and fizzy drinks! As you can imagine, this did nothing to get me back to normal.

This problem really started to take its toll on me. I was excessively tired and constantly bloated, and I was finding that I was less confident in myself due to the size of my stomach. Sometimes it got so bad my clothes didn't fit, and this was a source of great anxiety for me. Finally, I was beginning to understand I needed to take things into my own hands. However, the journey to eating well didn't start overnight. It was a gradual process of trial and a lot of errors. As I told you before, I am a naturally fussy eater so I don't enjoy eating what I don't like or eating for the sake of eating. If I am to eat it has to be what I love or nothing.

The first time I really started to enjoy my food was when I started work, where there was a wonderful canteen, and my colleagues encouraged me to try different things. There was also a juice bar, which I adored, and this meant that with very little effort on my part, I was consuming far more fresh fruit and vegetables than I had been. Eating with friends and trying different foods was a revelation to me, as hitherto I had stuck to eating what I knew, and as it was so limited, I either ate alone or with my family. Suddenly, I seemed to have a lot more energy than I used to. But even then, I didn't pay too much attention to the relationship between healthy eating and better health – though I knew it existed – all I knew was that I was enjoying the food.

WHAT TO EAT WHEN YOU HAVE SICKLE CELL

The first time I actually made a conscious decision to change my eating habits was when I was about to get married and I was encouraged to really take my diet in hand. I was determined not only to be well enough to actually turn up to my wedding, but also to find a way to reduce the bloating in my stomach, which was caused by the ever-present constipation, so I started to read a lot about nutrition, particularly what foods are important for sickle cell sufferers, and the foods to eat if you have constipation.

Dr Norman Parker, my consultant haematologist at Whittington Health who was so instrumental in helping improve my mental attitude, also needs to take huge credit for my change in eating habits. He was such an advocate of healthy eating, and relentlessly nagged all his patients about their diet, patiently explaining again and again why it is important to eat healthily and not just live off junk food. Even at his funeral, he couldn't let it rest, and he left a message to be read to his patients: 'If there are any patients here today tell them I have requested fruit be left in my coffin. I suspect it will not benefit me in my present state but I have always been a bit of an optimist.' He was a truly wonderful and caring doctor to whom I owe so much. It is thanks to him that I start every day with fresh fruit – how could I not? I would hate to disappoint him!

He taught me that sickle cell sufferers need food that will give us plenty of energy as our bodies burn calories at a higher rate, and we can become easily fatigued. So, certainly for me, the most effective diet is one that focuses on fruits, vegetables, whole grains, legumes and carbohydrates. Incorporating plenty of these foods into my diet is the most effective way to keep up my energy levels and immune system. Nigerian cuisine is something that I can still incorporate frequently into my diet – for example, I really enjoy jollof rice with tomato sauce and yams as they have a high starch and carbohydrate content which is beneficial to my often-fatigued body.

Food that is high in omega-3 fatty acids can also be beneficial for sickle cell sufferers, so eating lots of fish and foods such as walnuts or soy beans keeps down my cholesterol and makes my body feel energised and more active. In addition, if you have constipation, it is important to eat more high-fibre foods such as fresh fruit and vegetables and cereals, as well as trying to drink several glasses of water or other non-alcoholic liquid each day.

Sufferers also need a lot of protein. Whenever I consume fish and meat it makes me feel a lot stronger and healthier, especially after I've experienced a sickle cell crisis. I try to stick to leaner cuts of meats as it reduces the amount of fat. Grilling meats and fish is my favourite way to eat them and grilling channels off the excess cooking fats.

I must also make sure that I eat regularly and that each meal contains the right balance of vitamins and minerals and I would advise anyone who suffers from a chronic illness to do the same. Taking mineral and vitamin supplements is another effective way to maintain balance in my diet. Sickle cell sufferers have low levels of vitamin A, B6, C, E and carotenoids. This results is a significant deficiency of antioxidants, which can often be a cause of crises. Many studies have shown that certain vitamins such as Vitamin A, C and E, married with a combination of high-dose antioxidants which includes plenty of fruits and vegetables, can reduce the amount of sickled red blood cells, so it is imperative that I make sure these are part of my daily diet.

Eating a balanced diet should ensure that you have consumed the required vitamins and minerals needed, however, I routinely take a multi-vitamin and calcium to ensure I have the balance correct and to protect my bones from osteoporosis in later life.

I also take a cocktail of folic acid, penicillin V, vitamin B12 and calcium, although for the last three years I have limited this and have not taken them as often, instead I have tried to ensure that I get the right amount of vitamins in my food. In addition, I must be sure that I abide by the rule of eating little and often by enforcing a regimented schedule.

So, to help ensure I was healthy for my wedding, and with Dr Parker's advice, my family and I came up with an eating plan that I hoped would go some way to keeping me healthy enough to walk down the aisle. Since then I've pretty much stuck to this, only altering it every so often to provide variety. And here it is:

ANNE'S EATING PLAN

Breakfast
I am not a big fan of breakfast as it makes me too full and uncomfortable to be able to go about with my day. Also earlier in the day, I find that I can't digest anything too acidic. So during the week, I tend to keep it light.
- To begin with I have a ginger, lime and lemon shot first thing in the morning with two glasses of water. This gets my system moving and helps me to start

the day. The shot is simply a blend of one ginger root, one lime and one lemon with hot water to calm the acidity.

- Fruit and yoghurt smoothies – The yoghurt is really important for sickle cell sufferers as it helps to reduce acid in the blood. My two favourites are a banana, strawberry and blueberry smoothie, or a mango, avocado and apple smoothie. Sometimes I will go all green with green apples, spinach, cucumber, kale, limes, kiwi and yoghurt (all 100 per cent no sugar).
- Oatmeal – Sometimes I will make oatmeal with no milk, just water and put in some banana and honey for sweetening. I will have this with a slice of wholegrain bread with no butter (just because I don't like it much, plus it has a high fat content) and if I am really hungry, I will add a boiled egg and some smoked salmon.

At weekends, I tend to have a bigger breakfast, as I love a good lie-in so don't usually have breakfast until about 11am. At these times, I will go for a full English breakfast, or anything with a lot of protein and vegetables. I try to avoid processed foods as much as possible so my Full English usually has a bit of a twist. The foods I like to include are:
- Boiled Potatoes (no chips!)
- Fried eggs – I use extra virgin olive oil or groundnut oil
- Baked beans
- Mushrooms
- Grilled tomatoes

Lunch
Lunch is normally my heaviest meal of the day, and I will eat it any time between 12pm and 5pm. I don't regiment my times

because I eat whenever my body craves food. I tend to go for healthier options or Nigerian foods like:

- Salmon, brown rice and lots of green vegetables
- Chicken, carrots, peas and potatoes
- Baked potatoes with cheese and tuna and sweetcorn with a bowl of fruit salad, which will include apples, grapes and oranges
- African jollof rice, grilled red meat and lots of steamed vegetables such as carrots and peas
- Black-eyed beans, pottage and codfish stew made with lots of tomatoes
- Soup made from lots of okra and vegetables and steamed fish with pounded yam
- Edikang Ikong soup and boiled rice
- Plantain and black-eyed beans pottage
- Moi moi and custard

At the weekend I tend to eat lunch later and go for something lighter as I've usually had a big breakfast so at these times, I will normally go for something like chicken Caesar salad or salmon and lots of green vegetables.

Supper

I have to be very careful in the evenings or I will be very bloated and constipated in the morning, so I will only eat very light food such as:

- Salad
- Grilled chicken and green beans
- Minestrone soup
- Lettuce cups and beans
- Tomato soup
- Thai ground turkey lettuce cups
- Beans and greens with Parmesan polenta

Before bed, I also drink two litres of water. Although this has its own, obvious, side effect, it's essential for helping to dilute my blood.

Snacks

Taken in moderation, snacks prevent cravings and over-eating, and because sickle cell sufferers need to eat little and often, I always have a supply of nuts and fruit with me in case I need an energy boost to keep me going until my next meal. The worst types of snacks have abnormally high sugar content so sadly no sweets or pastries allowed, nor crisps, because of the fat.

THE BENEFITS OF HEALTHY EATING

Taking care of yourself when you have sickle cell or any illness is absolutely essential. Diet is important for everyone's quality of life, but it is particularly so for those of us who live with this disease. The benefits of sticking to this eating plan have been manifold for me. Not only has it reduced the number of crises I was suffering, probably because I am healthier all round and less prone to infections and colds, but it also means I have more energy to play with my children and to take exercise – I'll come to that! In addition, my skin has cleared up, and my IBS has almost completely disappeared.

That's not to say that it's always easy. I frequently crave the odd deep-fried calamari or battered fish, but I know that I must be extra careful when it comes to what I eat as I do not want anything to potentially trigger a crisis. Even so, like anyone I have 'cheat days' and one thing I cannot resist is puff-puff. This is an African snack that is essentially a fried dough ball, similar to a doughnut. I really enjoy them in small doses and they give me that extra sugar boost I sometimes need. However, I must remind myself not to over-indulge.

EATING AFTER A CRISIS

Maintaining a healthy diet can be very difficult at the best times, but I find it especially hard when I experience a crisis. When you feel low in hospital and your body is weak, you often crave food that is bad for you because it is comforting.

There is nothing wrong with wanting to treat yourself occasionally, especially when you have just had a dose of illness, however I have to remind myself not to get carried away. I have had some of the most bizarre cravings while in hospital and my family really have wonderful patience when it comes to meeting my odd demands, bringing me a range of meals from spinach soup, rice and beans to hamburgers, fried chicken and fries. These have provided me with simple pleasures at times of depression. It's hard to eat after a crisis sometimes as our appetite tends to be reduced, so it's much better to eat something rather than nothing at all. If you're craving a particular food when you are ill, indulge yourself.

But once you are back home and your appetite has improved, try not to allow yourself to slip back into bad eating habits. It's not always easy, but here are some things I do to try to keep me on track:

STICKING TO YOUR EATING PLAN NO MATTER WHAT

- Do not be afraid to ask your friends and family to help you prepare packed meals that you love, especially when you are ill.
- I try not to be too prescriptive, because sometimes your body craves a certain food, so don't deprive yourself, as long as it's not an obviously unhealthy choice.
- After a stay in hospital my taste buds are usually dulled from the drugs, so try to ensure plenty of flavour to tempt yourself. Once your immune system

has recovered, your taste buds will too.

- No matter what, always try to drink a lot. This is sometimes hard for me when I have just left the hospital so I have tried to find a variety of drinks that I like that are not high in sugar such as lemon juice, green tea or pomegranate juice.
- Sometimes when your appetite is flagging and you are finding it difficult to eat, it helps to eat in company. This is not only enjoyable but it encourages you to eat more. So pester your friends and family to come for a meal.
- Be realistic with your eating plan. Only include food you know you like, and don't leave long intervals between eating.
- Always carry snacks! The medicine I take makes my stomach feel funny, so I need to snack regularly. But also, when you travel or when you have a busy day that might entail eating later than you normally would, it's essential you have something to keep you going. For me, this is usually fruit and nuts.
- This might not work for everyone, but a picture of my stomach at its most bloated due to IBS is a great motivator for me. It's a visual reminder of why I need to stick to the plan.
- Try not to have unhealthy food in the house. Now I have children, this is no longer realistic, though, as I don't want to deprive my children. So I have given them set times when they can have their snacks, and I make sure I am a long way away so I'm not tempted!
- When your diet is limited, it's easy to get bored. So try to find ways to vary your food, and always look out for new and tempting recipes.
- Don't deprive yourself of eating out, but do plan

before you go. I tend to check the menu before I go to make sure there is something I can eat.

- If your life is busy, plan and cook your food for the week at the weekend. That way, if you come home exhausted, you don't have to worry about what you're going to eat.

If you have a long journey planned – particularly a long flight – make sure you take your own food with you. Alternatively, you can ring the airline and pre-order food from their menu.

CHAPTER 31

TAKING YOUR MEDICINE

Alongside the healthy diet, of course, there are various drugs that need to be taken to help keep us healthy, and I want to talk now about adhering not only to a healthy diet, but also to the medical regime that the doctors prescribe for you. It seems ridiculous to many who do not live with a chronic illness that anyone would struggle to take their prescribed drugs, because for most people, when they are ill they take the drugs, get better, and get on with their lives. For those of us living with chronic illness, however, there is no end to it. We *always* have to take our medicine, and usually our regime involves a complex cocktail of drugs that need to be taken in specific quantities at specific times. And because there are often so many drugs, and so many different times and quantities, it can become confusing, and most of all, it is boring! Sticking to a medical regimen exactly as a doctor prescribes sounds easy, but personally, I struggle to find the motivation to take my daily recommended drugs. And yet if I don't, I risk falling ill.

This lack of motivation is always a big concern with me, and even though I know exactly why I need to take the drugs, I think sometimes because the drugs are maintaining health, rather than curing you, the benefits of taking them are not immediately evident. This only happens when you stop taking them for a while, so day in and day out you just feel like you're popping pills and sticking to rules that seem to add nothing to your life. In fact, sometimes they restrict you by interrupting your day or causing unwelcome side effects.

For many who live in countries where they don't have the benefit of a good health system, there is the added problem of the expense. Prescription drugs are expensive and one has to justify to oneself the value of spending this amount of money on drugs when the immediate benefits are not visible. Cost can be a major factor in non-adherence because when you can't afford to fill your prescriptions, you might decide to take less than the prescribed dose so you can make the prescription last longer, even though we know very well that to get the best results, it is essential to take the medicine as instructed.

It seems that I am not in a minority when it comes to struggling to stick to my prescriptions, and, aside from the cost, a major contributing factor to this is perhaps a lack of clarity, and ambiguity, about how to take the medicine, especially when we are prescribed several medicines with different schedules. And after years and years of taking medicines, we can become careless and lackadaisical about following the instructions – particularly when those instructions are complex.

It is very challenging to take several medicines with different schedules. For example, I might have to take some in the morning, or afternoon at a specific time, then again in the evening, and, to be honest, it can be time-consuming and tedious.

Then, when you add to that some of the unpleasant side effects that certain medications can give you, this just adds to the drudgery, and if you are feeling well, and see no benefit in continuing to take the drug, it's easy to just 'forget' to continue.

For me, this is the main reason why I am not always consistent with my daily medication routine, even though I know that doing so is important to control my sickle cell disease and improve my overall long-term health and well-being.

So, to try to break myself of this habit, I have devised some strategies and tips to help me stick to the regime by incorporating it into my lifestyle.

Here's what I do:

- I have fostered a good relationship with my pharmacists because I find them very helpful – particularly when it comes to asking questions about the benefits of, and an explanation of, the medicine schedule.

- Every night before I go to bed I prepare my daily medicine for the next day, including both morning and evening dose. Thus, I try to take it at the same time in the morning and evening – always with my breakfast in the morning, and just before I go to bed in the evening.

- I maintain a weekly medicine container for morning and evening and have set reminders on my phone for when I should take my dose.

- To maintain consistency, I try to refill my medicine container at the same time each week. For example, every Sunday morning after breakfast.

- It is hard to keep a routine when travelling, but when I am away, I ensure that I carry enough of my medication, plus a few days extra in case my return is delayed or I have to stay a bit longer. Also, I always keep the medication in my hand luggage, particularly when flying, in case my suitcases are lost.

CHAPTER 32

YES, YOU *CAN* EXERCISE

As with all healthy lifestyles, keeping fit is essential. Regular exercise is wonderful for building up stamina, which helps people manage crises much more effectively. It is a fact that the better shape you are in, the quicker your recovery time can be. This is easier said than done when you suffer from sickle cell, however, because exercise for sicklers can often be a catalyst for a crisis due to the difficulties with oxygen levels in the blood that sickle cell causes.

It is here where the frustration often lies with me and my attitude to exercise. I find that if I try to go running or walk for too long I begin to feel my body react negatively and I grow anxious that I might have a crisis. Sickle cell sufferers become fatigued quickly during exercise, which really limits the amount one can do, so it can be difficult to find the right exercise for you, and this in turn leads to inertia and stops you taking any exercise at all.

Unfortunately, this means that we often have low levels of endurance, which can make a crisis last longer and the recovery slower. It can be a vicious circle.

To be honest, I never did any kind of exercise as a child, or even as an adult, until recently. In fact, it's only been in the last year that I have plucked up the courage to exercise. I was often discouraged by my family who were terrified I would hurt myself (see Chapter 26 about training your loved ones!). My mother was the worst. She was worried about me doing even the most basic exercise, including going for short walks. In a way I understood where she was coming from as most times I could barely walk over a hundred yards so how could someone as weak as me be able to do the hard-core exercise that she saw people doing at the gym, such as running on treadmills, lifting weights and boxing?

She just could not see her sick daughter doing any of this. Especially as my mother was well aware that even gentle walks outside could bring on a crisis. It would start with a numbness in my mouth and progress into my head. It would feel as if all circulation had been cut off from my face, and only taking painkillers would alleviate this.

I remember going for a fitness test at the hospital after I had had a terrible bout of pneumonia, which had left me in intensive care for a few days, and as I expected the results were not great at all. I had the fitness level of a very old, inactive lady. This I already knew, as I was unable to walk for more than a hundred yards or do anything without help. But even then, I didn't take the steps I should have done to change this. I was too scared and convinced that a gym was a place only for fit people, not people like me who struggled to lift anything heavier than a bag of sugar.

This mindset started to change when a colleague and I were sent to deliver some letters on behalf of a client. We only had to walk a very short distance, but I noticed I was very slow and just couldn't keep up no matter how hard I tried. My colleague was shocked. 'Anne,' he said. 'I am walking as slow as I can. Can you really not keep up?'

As we sat down to rest so I could catch my breath, he told

me that he had type 2 diabetes due to his poor lifestyle choices. He explained that he had refused to listen to the doctors who told him he needed to change his lifestyle, until he had become so sick, he nearly died. When he got better, he made the life-changing decision to always take care of his health first and he now went to the gym regularly to keep fit.

At this time, I was still prone to bouts of self-pity and his words, rather than inspiring me, actually made me feel very sorry for myself, especially as I felt completely foolish about not being able to even walk down the street. However, in truth, he did plant one of the seeds that helped me turn my life around, and I decided to join the gym and try to get fitter. Unfortunately, I overdid it, and the next day I was in hospital so I felt it was a waste of my time and cancelled my membership after three months, as I still had not gained the courage to visit the gym again. If only I could have swallowed my pride and asked for help, things might have been very different, but I was stubborn and unwilling to open up to help at that time.

Years later as I got much older and, thanks to my diet, the frequency of my sickle cell crises reduced, I again started to think about keeping fit. The interest grew more after having my second baby, as I wanted to be in my best shape, and find a way to lose my 'mummy tummy'. Also, I had given up my disability badge, so I couldn't rely on being able to park close to my destination anymore. I *needed* to be fitter.

But I can't deny the thought made me nervous. All the bad memories came back to haunt me – the tennis courts, the swimming pool, the various cancelled gym memberships… I had many bad memories associated with exercise, but I decided the time had come when I needed to trust myself more. So I went to buy gym clothes that I liked as a kind of a motivation. But even though I looked the part, as I approached the gym, my heart started to beat faster: what if people laughed when they saw how unfit I was, or that I didn't know how to use any of the gym equipment? I know! No one cares, but I think I was looking for excuses to back out. Luckily I forced myself to go inside where I found everyone to be incredibly friendly, and they recommended I get a personal trainer. This was so obvious, I have no idea why I'd never considered it before. It was also one of the best decisions I have ever made.

The problem was though, when he met me my trainer thought I was already fit and needed to be pushed further. Like all sickle cell sufferers I am naturally thin, and actually *look* quite fit. And, in my nervousness, I didn't disabuse him. To my utter mortification, and his alarm, after ten minutes I almost fainted despite the fact we had only been doing very basic exercises. He had to take me into a quiet room so I could lie down and recover. It was at this point, I finally told him about my sickle cell. Top tip to any of my fellow sufferers – if you get a personal trainer, be sure to make them aware of your condition *before* you start!

To his credit, he was sweet and very keen to understand more about sickle cell and how it affected my workout. And before I went back to see him, he researched the condition thoroughly, coming up with exercises he thought I'd be able to manage and which would help me build strength and stamina.

Despite the fainting episode, I left the gym full of hope. I was also pleased that I had actually managed to do ten minutes of exercise because considering how weak and unfit I was, this felt like a real achievement to me.

The next time I went, my trainer had written an exercise plan for me that would not overstretch me and bring on a crisis, but would increase my fitness, and would also be fun. To begin with I did gentle warm-up exercises to ensure my temperature was regulated, and then we began. At first the exercises were very gentle, such as lifting 2kg weights, the leg press machine with no weights, jogging inside around the gym, walking on the treadmill, rowing at a slow pace and some abs work but without any weights.

I needed to make sure I went back regularly – at least four times a week – because there is no benefit otherwise, and if I took a break it was hard on my body to start back again. Although I was quite stiff and achy to begin with, I immediately noticed some benefits. For example, I was sleeping much better, I was more alert and I also had much more energy – which is always useful when you have two small children.

As my fitness increased, I started learning what worked and what didn't work for someone with sickle cell. I also learned, with the help of my trainer, to always listen to my body, but not to be afraid to try something new because it's only by pushing yourself a little that you will start seeing the changes you want.

For example, I discovered that I really enjoy boxing as I feel in charge when I'm doing this. It's a good workout that covers all the body areas and provides a useful balance. I also enjoy working on my abs by doing things like sit ups as I really wanted to work on that area, and to my delight I noticed improvements very quickly, which helped motivate me to keep going back. And the weightlifting helps me build my muscles and strengthen my joints, improving my mobility. In fact, I started to enjoy my gym visits so much, and this made the exercising easier. When you are happy doing something, it never feels like such an effort.

What I also discovered is that exercise helped me enormously in managing the problems and symptoms that I was already experiencing with my sickle cell, such as extreme fatigue and the persistent pain I usually have all over my joints, especially in my shoulder. I noticed that as my strength and flexibility started to increase, the joint pain reduced. And it wasn't just physically where I noticed an improvement. Mentally I was having less mood swings and I had a much more positive attitude towards trying new things.

By the third month my confidence was growing and I was getting stronger. I saw that I was not the only person at the gym who was weak and tired and it made me realise how ridiculous it was for me to have been so embarrassed the first time I went. The gym is not just for people who are already fit, it is also for people trying to get fit and others, like me, who are unwell and need to build their strength.

Although having sickle cell means that there may be times when symptoms flare up and working out just isn't possible, and also there will be times when you are too tired and you need to stay away, if you keep your visits as regular as possible, you will be amazed how much better you can feel.

EXERCISES

There are some exercises that may not be suitable for sickle cell sufferers. For me, swimming falls into this category, but as long as you can regulate your temperature and keep warm, there is no reason why others might not find it enjoyable. My gym routine is focused on aerobic exercises, as this is the best way to keep your heart strong. Also, you need to work the larger muscles in the body which will help to increase your endurance and strength.

So, after some trial and error, my trainer has come up with a series of exercises that work for me:

To begin
1   Walking, mild stretching or light jumping. Also mild strengthening exercises like lifting a one-pound dumbbell.

When you get a bit stronger

2   Low-impact aerobic exercises such as fast walking, stretching and yoga.

3   Moving gradually on to boxing, jumping jacks, wall sits, abdominal crunches, squats, planks, rowing and anything to keep my heartbeat going and blood circulating.

4   I complete my workout by doing a full-body stretch.

The whole workout lasts no longer than twenty to thirty minutes maximum. Any more and I run the risk of getting too tired.

Of course, we also tried some exercises that didn't suit me. For example, weightlifting – unless the weights are tiny – step-ups onto a chair or doing push ups, because my arms simply aren't strong enough. Also, I cannot take classes, as no matter how hard I try I can't keep up, and I'm much better working at my own pace with my trainer. Though I am much fitter, I know that I will never be as fit as somebody who doesn't have sickle cell. But I have discovered this doesn't mean I can't be fit in terms of a person with my condition. And now that I have discovered exercises that don't put me at risk of being ill, I am finding the experience incredibly rewarding. I just wish I'd had the courage to try it sooner.

OVERCOMING YOUR FEAR

Before I started, I was terrified of going to the gym, for the many reasons I have already stated. In addition, my fitness had been so poor for so long that I couldn't see a way it could ever improve without causing me pain or making me ill. You need to overcome these fears, but it's not always easy. So here's what I suggest:

•   Talk to your doctor about what exercise is suitable for you, especially if you are frequently unwell. They can provide advice on the level of intensity that's safe for you, as well as how long your exercise sessions should last and how many times per week you should be exercising.

- Review your medicine. Some medicines cause light-headedness and tiredness, or they may have other side effects that you're unaware of. So speak to the doctor about whether your medications are suitable for an exercise programme and if not, whether there are better solutions that will work for you.

- Have a fitness test before you start, so you know just how far you can push your body, and which joints will be problematic. This is so important for sickle cell sufferers because, as you know, many years of sickle cell crises causes long-term damage to the joints and the bones, so you need to be careful.

- Don't go alone. If at all possible, use a personal trainer. They will devise a safe plan for you and will also be there to help motivate you. Plus, it's always a good idea to have someone with you at the gym in case you get unwell. If you can't get a personal trainer, then perhaps see if there's a friend who would be happy to be your gym buddy.

- Stick to a pace and intensity that works for you. Never try to keep up with anyone else.

- Focus on the exercises and routine you enjoy, and discard those that bring you discomfort or don't feel right for your body.

- Always keep in mind why you are going to the gym. By improving your fitness, you improve your overall health, and this should not only reduce the number of hospital visits, but also mean that, if you do get sick, your recovery time will be much quicker as your body is better equipped to cope. And all of this frees up your time to spend with your loved ones and do the things you love.

By taking control of my lifestyle, I have taken further responsibility for my illness and I am much better off for doing so. However, a word of warning, it is vital to try and stay consistent and committed to your diet and fitness needs at all times. It is never easy to start, but once you have, and you see the benefits, you will wonder why you didn't try it before.

TIPS FOR A HEALTHY LIFESTYLE TO HELP REDUCE SICKLE CELL SYMPTOMS

1 **Get organised.** Before going to bed, create a to-do list for the next day. This will include what you will be eating, your medication and when you will exercise – whether at the gym or at home. This way you build in the time you need around all your other everyday tasks, and it will help you stay consistent to your regime.

2 **Plan and prepare your meals for the week at the weekend.** This will help you stay on-track, and save time during the busy working week. I have found it is far too easy to divert from healthy eating when I don't already have a meal plan because I am too tired to think about it after a day at work. Remember, people with chronic illness tend to always be tired so the less pressure we put on ourselves the easier it is to overcome whatever battle we are fighting.

3 **Always be in control of your workout and find individuals that are flexible to work with you.** For example, having a personal trainer has been the best strategy for me, as it helps motivate me, but also when you have someone who understands you and what you are going through, it relieves the stress of wondering what will happen should you become ill at the gym. Always remember you are only as fit

or healthy as your mind, so the less anxiety you have about the gym visits, the more positive and determined you will be to improve your fitness.

I wish with all my heart that healthy eating and exercise could cure sickle cell, but of course it can't. But for me, the benefits of being strict with myself about working out and eating healthily have been unimaginable. I can't say whether I would have had the self-control to be quite so dedicated to a healthy lifestyle when I was younger, but if I had I would have avoided so much pain and sickness. However, it's never too late to start, as I have discovered. Nor too early. In fact, the earlier the better. I wish that as a child I had been given all of this information and all these tools to help me, because my life might have been a lot easier.

But as it is, I am grateful to have arrived at this point where my crises have reduced, I am able to walk further, and I have enough energy to run (well, maybe not run!) around the house after my children. Something that I couldn't have imagined being possible just a few years ago.

CHAPTER 33

KEEP FIGHTING LIKE A WARRIOR

Sickle cell is a difficult disease to come to terms with, especially because the future for most sufferers remains uncertain. I myself am unsure how long I will have to deal with this illness. Yet I know that I need to fight it with dedication and positivity, because I don't have any other choice. As I said before, I need to take baby steps every single day to keep this illness from bogging me down.

Learning to change my attitude has made a whole lot of difference. I accept the fact that I will need to live with this illness for the rest of my life and have made peace with it. The moment you do that, you pave the way for happiness amidst all travails. Once I acknowledged this to myself, I became comfortable saying 'No' to things I knew very well I couldn't do. Understanding my limitations did not turn out to be a weakness at all; it became my strength because I began to understand more about what I could do and started to focus on just that.

Whenever I am well, I try to live in the moment rather than making frantic attempts to eliminate pain. Yes, pain management is crucial, but pain is inevitable in cases like mine, so I need to take my mind off that by taking painkillers that work.

No day is perfect; for example, walking still causes me problems – although less than it used to – but rather than excluding something I love from my daily life, I work towards controlling the pain by taking the medication.

Living with a chronic illness can make you feel helpless. But once you realise you are not alone, nor are you helpless, that knowledge can empower you to make positive changes in your life that can help you stay as strong as possible.

The simplest changes you can make are in lifestyle: eating healthily, taking physical exercise and listening to your body, so you can predict when you are about to get ill and take steps to minimise the effects.

The harder part is finding happiness despite your pain. I've talked at length about that, but in summary, for me, this has meant doing the following:

- Surrounding myself with people I love.
- I've stopped striving to win the approval of others; this only ever made me anxious.
- Taking care of myself well and never letting my illness prevent me from seeking what really makes me happy from within. It is *my* life and no matter how hard it is, I know I need to make the most of whatever opportunities I am presented with. Life is a glorious gift from God. There is no point squandering it.
- I have focused on my spirituality. This has been a great help to me in getting to the core of who I am. By becoming more prayerful and increasing my faith in God, I learned to believe that my problems would become manageable. For others, there will be other spiritual paths that might help, but I have found my faith has given me a peace and acceptance that in turn helps to sustain my mental health.

One of the most miraculous things for me since I have really taken control of my disease and my pain, is that I have not had a major crisis for nearly two years. I know that I may have one at any time, but I also know that I can get through it. And by letting go of the anxiety I always had, and taking steps to prevent more pain in terms of my lifestyle choices and my mindset, I firmly believe that I have kept the worst at bay.

While I don't claim to have conquered all the challenges that confront me, I know that I will never stop trying. There have been a number of occasions in my life when sickle cell has made me feel powerless, but focusing my mind on my career and my potentially bright future helped me loosen its grip on me. It was a Herculean task, one I was never sure I could succeed at, but I did it, and though I know that I will continue to suffer all the pain that is synonymous with sickle cell, I also know how to fight it out like a warrior. And more than that, I now know I am capable of a great deal more than just handling an illness that has stymied my life in more ways than one. I still have a tough battle on my hands, but I am ready.

LIVING WITH AN INVISIBLE ILLNESS

Having sickle cell has affected my life. It is hard to explain to someone with no idea of the difficulties we face. It is an everyday haul to cope with the pain, the weakness and the contradiction of feeling awful on the inside while looking perfectly fine on the outside. Definitely more needs to be done to help sufferers cope with their daily struggles, especially when it comes to dealing with and managing their pain. Also, society at large imperatively needs to understand this and learn to be less judgemental when someone with an invisible illness tells them that they are unwell.

The truth is that the majority of times we feel guilty for being in this position and not being able to fit in. We feel very alone with our limitations because we are not able to do all the things our friends and family are doing. We feel depressed and anxious as we are unsure of tomorrow.

Sickle cell is never predictable and the pain during a sickle cell crisis makes it difficult for us to get out of bed, make work plans or have a normal life. We rarely remember our first sickle cell crisis, because there are so many of them and sometimes even doctors fail to understand what we are going through, especially when you visit a doctor who doesn't have an understanding of your condition.

I remember when I first understood the gravity of my struggles of living with sickle cell it was so overwhelming that I had trouble managing them. A lack of understanding of the associated pain meant that I was daily in and out of the hospital. This was because I wanted to fit in and engage in the same activities as my sisters and friends, which in turn caused me great harm. This behaviour also made me quit a job after only one day as my body was in shock. The manager could not comprehend why I needed my desk area to be at a set temperature. I also noticed that several people avoided me, as I couldn't keep up with their demands.

But the more we talk about these issues, the less sufferers feel alone. We need to exploit both online and offline avenues to increase this information-sharing. This dialogue will inform more and more people and will hopefully foster a better understanding of how we are feeling. And so I will never stop believing in the power of talking and sharing information on this rarely talked about disease.

Invisible illnesses are real, and society needs to understand that although we might be perfect outside, a closer look inside will tell a different story. Of course, having the support of your loved ones and doctors helps reduce our suffering enormously, and for them, the information available, and the understanding of the disease has improved in leaps and bounds since I was a child, but we sufferers cannot live in a cocoon if we want to live a full and active life, participating in and contributing to society. So we need a wider understanding of what we are going through, and hopefully, gradually, attitudes will change.

Living with this disease has really affected my life, and many people just don't understand what the effects have been, nor what I require. And when we are sick, many just don't know how to treat you, nor do they have the patience or desire to enquire too closely.

I hope that by telling my story, I will have given hope to other sufferers as well as having given a greater understanding of the condition to anyone who either knows someone with sickle cell or someone with any other invisible illness that requires special care.

Because, in the end, all we need is love from people, hope for tomorrow and motivation to go through every day.

CONCLUSION

I want the readers of this book, especially those with chronic invisible illnesses, to find happiness from knowing that challenges can be overcome and life can be filled with joy.

I hope that by writing about my life with sickle cell I can raise awareness in general about this horrible condition. But as well as sickle cell sufferers, there are many other people around the world who suffer from other incurable non-communicable diseases, and I hope that my advice can be useful for them too, and will help them find a way to manage their disease and live fairly comfortably, happily and with joy for the rest of their lives.

This can only be achieved by first ensuring that those around them have an understanding of what they are going through and, of course, that they have access to good medical care.

More importantly, for all involved, they need to try to keep a positive attitude at all times. This will help foster resilience and will hopefully speed recovery time after an illness.

But, in the end it is not enough for just those involved to be understanding. If the wider world in general understood the burden of non-communicable diseases, and therefore the needs of people who suffer from them, it would go a long way towards easing their daily lives. This is sometimes a matter of life and death, because a negative attitude towards someone with sickle cell can depress and actually kill them. This might sound drastic, but it is the reality of our lives.

After all, nobody enjoys one hundred per cent good health, and many people have suffered from bouts of ill health at one time or another. The difference is, for those of us with chronic conditions, our situation will not change. But still, our lives can be lived to the fullest with faith and trust in God, faith and confidence in ourselves, and with the support and understanding of family, friends and loved ones. And, of course, with access to doctors who understand how to treat us.

And to you, my fellow sufferers, I urge you to not hide your situation, because, not only can it be dangerous for you, it is nothing to be ashamed of. Instead, grab life with both hands and live the life you want socially, professionally, religiously and communally. Never think that because you have sickle cell that your life cannot be full of love and happiness. Or even a family of your own. The disease does not stand in the way of enjoying married life, but be sure to pick an understanding partner who loves you just as you are.

Let nobody determine the agenda of your life, because you are your own master. Have objectives and targets and incrementally, with baby steps, follow them. You are an achiever because there is the spirit of a hero or heroine in you. Whatever your physical situation is, you are created in the image of God, and you must live to fulfil the purpose of God for creating you.

ACKNOWLEDGEMENTS

I would like to thank all the people who have joined me on my journey of living with sickle cell, my invisible illness.

My beautiful parents, Nancy and Eric, who have never questioned the belief that I will succeed in life. The sacrifices each has made to ensure that I continue to prosper are priceless.

My wonderful sisters, Catherine and Sarah, who I have grown up with. Without their love and support I would not have had the courage to battle on.

The loves of my life: my kids, Connor and Caroline, who give my life meaning. To my sisters' babies: Christopher, Charlotte and Chloe, who call me Mummy Anne. The happiness they bring me every day is the most powerful potion for fighting sickle cell that can be given.

Marvin, my supportive husband, for his unwavering belief and support of me. It is hard to believe that as I write this book, we have been together for nineteen years and yet the journey becomes more magical each and every day.

Meagan and Sierra, his lovely girls and my stepdaughters. I have known them as long as Marvin and they continue to amaze me as they chart their own life journeys – always closely tied to what happens in each other's lives.

My extended family of aunties and uncles. In Nigerian culture the extended family is extremely close and regardless of where in the world we are located their good wishes follow me.

My strong network of friends who have had an impact on my daily life and who continue to look upon me as a person striving to succeed in life: not as a disabled person but instead as one of absolute determination.

Over the years I have had some wonderful work colleagues who have been understanding from the beginning. Their belief in me and their compassion and recognition of my condition gave me the confidence and determination to succeed.

All the wonderful medical practitioners who have helped me find a way to manage my disease. I would like to pay special tribute to Dr Porter and Dr Parker who have really helped me understand the technical aspects of my disease.

I would like to give a special mention to the former President of Nigeria, Olusegun Obasanjo, who was always accepting of my illness and helpful in improving the quality of my life. His guidance has made the difference in choosing the difficult options presented to me and in return overcoming challenges I would never have dreamed possible.